Advanced Quality Auditing

Also available from ASQ Quality Press:

eAuditing Fundamentals: Virtual Communication and Remote Auditing
J.P. Russell and Shauna Wilson

The ASQ Auditing Handbook, Fourth Edition
J.P. Russell, editor

The Process Auditing and Techniques Guide, Second Edition
J.P. Russell

Quality Audits for Improved Performance, Third Edition
Dennis R. Arter

The Internal Auditing Pocket Guide: Preparing, Performing, Reporting and Follow-up, Second Edition
J.P. Russell

Auditing Beyond Compliance: Using the Portable Universal Quality Lean Audit Model
Janet Bautista-Smith

AS9101D Auditing for Process Performance: Combining Conformance and Effectiveness to Meet Customer Satisfaction
Chad Kymal

The Quality Toolbox, Second Edition
Nancy R. Tague

Mapping Work Processes, Second Edition
Bjørn Andersen, Tom Fagerhaug, Bjørnar Henriksen, and Lars E. Onsøyen

Root Cause Analysis: Simplified Tools and Techniques, Second Edition
Bjørn Andersen and Tom Fagerhaug

The Certified Manager of Quality/Organizational Excellence Handbook, Fourth Edition
Russell T. Westcott, editor

To request a complimentary catalog of ASQ Quality Press publications, call 800-248-1946, or visit our Web site at http://www.asq.org/quality-press.

Advanced Quality Auditing

An Auditor's Review of Risk Management, Lean Improvement, and Data Analysis

Lance B. Coleman, Sr.

ASQ Quality Press
Milwaukee, Wisconsin

American Society for Quality, Quality Press, Milwaukee, WI 53203
© 2015 by ASQ
All rights reserved. Published 2015.
Printed in the United States of America.

21   20   19   5   4   3

Library of Congress Cataloging-in-Publication Data

Coleman, Lance B., 1962–
Advanced quality auditing: an auditor's review of risk management,
lean improvement, and data analysis/Lance B. Coleman.
      pages cm
Includes bibliographical references.
ISBN 978-0-87389-913-0 (hardcover: alk. paper)
1. Quality control—Auditing. 2. Risk management. 3. Auditing,
Internal. 4. Industrial management. I. Title.
TS156.C6155 2015
658.5'62—dc23
                                    2015011925

Publisher: Lynelle Korte
Acquisitions Editor: Matt Meinholz
Managing Editor: Paul Daniel O'Mara
Production Administrator: Randall Benson

ASQ Mission: The American Society for Quality advances individual,
organizational, and community excellence worldwide through learning, quality
improvement, and knowledge exchange.

Attention Bookstores, Wholesalers, Schools, and Corporations: ASQ Quality
Press books, video, audio, and software are available at quantity discounts with
bulk purchases for business, educational, or instructional use. For information,
please contact ASQ Quality Press at 800-248-1946, or write to ASQ Quality Press,
P.O. Box 3005, Milwaukee, WI 53201-3005.

To place orders or to request ASQ membership information, call 800-248-1946.
Visit our Web site at www.asq.org/quality-press.

♾ Printed on acid-free paper

Quality Press
600 N. Plankinton Ave.
Milwaukee, WI 53203-2914
E-mail: authors@asq.org

ASQ   The Global Voice of Quality™

Dedication

I dedicate this book to my wife and family. My wife of 29 years, Lorraine continues to be a source of love, support, and inspiration in all that I do. My four children Larissa, Lauren, Lance Jr., and Latrice were a joy and blessing to raise; now as adults I am proud to call them friends. Finally a shout out to my dogs Auggie, Leo, and Shii whose boundless exuberance and joy upon my simply entering the house bring a burst of joy into even the most dismal of days that we all sometimes face.

Table of Contents

List of Figures and Tables . . . . *ix*

Foreword . . . . *xi*

Introduction . . . . *xiii*

Chapter 1: Traditional Audits 1
    What Makes a Good Audit? 2
    QMS Auditing 3
    Process Auditing 4
    Conducting the Audit 7
    Audit Closure 9

Chapter 2: Lean Auditing for Business Improvement 13
    Introduction to Lean Principles 13
    Plan-Do-Check-Act (PDCA) 17
    Integrating Lean Tools into the Audit Program 18
    Constructing a Lean Audit Checklist using the
        Audit Checklist Development Matrix 19
    Case in Point 2.1: Lean Receiving Audit 21
    Case in Point 2.2: Lean Logistics 24

Chapter 3: Risk-Based Quality Auditing (RBQA) 25
    What is Risk Management? 25
    Risk Assessment 28
    Risk Management Integration 33
    Risk-Based Quality Auditing 35
    Case in Point 3.1: Auditing for Risk 40

Chapter 4: Data and Trend Analysis **43**
   Statistical and Data Analysis Tools.   43
   How to Analyze Data Effectively   45
   Auditors and Data Analysis   46
   Case in Point 4.1: Measurable Goals and Objectives   47

Chapter 5: Root Cause Analysis and Corrective Action **49**
   How to Accomplish Successful Root Cause Analysis (RCA) . . .   49
   The Difference Between Corrective and Preventive Action   50
   RCA Tools.   50
   What are the Steps of the Corrective Action Process.   52
   How and When to Close a Corrective Action.   53
   Case in Point 5.1: Is / Is Not   54
   Case in Point 5.2: Traffic Accidents.   56

Chapter 6: How Delightful is Your Audit Program? **61**
   The Audit Function as a Service   61
   What Makes a Good Audit Program   61
   How to Objectively and Consistently Evaluate
      Your Audit Program   65
   Case in Point 6.1: Audit Program Based on Existing Records . .   70

Chapter 7: Audit Reporting. **77**

Chapter 8: Charting a Path Forward **79**
   Needed Skills.   79
   Steps Forward   81

Appendix **83**
   Basic Statistics   83
   Control Charts.   84

Bibliography *89*

Index *91*

List of Figures and Tables

Figure 1.1	L. O. C. k S	2
Figure 1.2	The *W* Factor	3
Figure 1.3	Process map	4
Figure 1.4	D. O. o R. S.	7
Table 1.1	Audit checklist template	9
Figure 2.1	PDCA cycle	18
Figure 2.2	Audit checklist development matrix (ACDM)	20
Case in Point 2.1	Lean receiving audit	21
Figure 2.3	Receiving process flowchart	21
Figure 2.4	Receiving value stream map	23
Case in Point 2.2	Lean logistics	24
Table 3.1	Risk matrix	29
Table 3.2	Risk assessment form risk matrix	30
Table 3.3	Likelihood of detection	30
Table 3.4	Defining likelihood	31
Table 3.5	Defining impact	31
Table 3.6	FMEA table	32
Table 3.7	Sample auditor risk management training matrix	34
Figure 3.1	Risk identification and response process flow	35
Table 3.8	Finding classification by risk	38
Figure 3.2	Hiring process map showing enablers and risks	39
Case in Point 3.1	Auditing for risk	40
Figure 4.1	Process	43
Case in Point 4.1	Measurable goals and objectives	47

Figure 5.1	Ishikawa diagram	52
Case in Point 5.1	Is/Is not.......................................	54
Table 5.1	Same/Not same................................	55
Case in Point 5.2	Traffic accidents	56
Figure 5.2	Car accident fishbone diagram	56
Table 5. 2	Traffic accident notes...........................	57
Figure 5.3	Scatter diagram of traffic volume vs. number of crashes	59
Figure 5.4	Pareto chart of potential cause..................	59
Figure 6.1	Kano diagram..................................	62
Table 6.1	Value add	65
Table 6.2	Reality check..................................	66
Figure 6.2	Audit program model...........................	67
Figure 6.3	Audit program evaluation form	69
Case in Point 6.1	Audit program based on existing records	70
Figure 6.4a	Audit program initial assessment.................	72
Figure 6.4b	Audit program post-improvement assessment	74
Figure 6.5	Audit program dashboard	76
Table 8.1	Job titles related to auditing functions	81
Table 8.2	Auditor self-assessment	82
Figure A.1	Sample control chart	85
Figure A.2	Control chart showing special cause variation	85

Foreword

This book has essential information that will help guide an organization's efforts to glean more value from their audit process. Coleman's forward thinking will help grow the audit function beyond verification audits.

The book provides insight for using the audit function to improve organizations using lean principles. He also discusses how the audit function can contribute and be integrated into the ongoing risk management program.

Verification of conformity to audit criteria is extremely important and must be done well. The practices discussed in the book provide us with a challenging opportunity to expand audit objectives and auditor competencies.

JP RUSSELL, ASQ FELLOW, CQA

Introduction

Audit: *"Systematic, independent and documented process for obtaining audit evidence and evaluating it objectively to determine the extent to which Audit criteria are fulfilled."*

ISO 190011: 2018
THE ASQ AUDITING HANDBOOK, 4TH EDITION

A group discussion was had during a recent Audit Division conference on whether auditing is a skill set or a profession such as accounting or engineering. I would suggest that it is both. Who wouldn't want to be able to walk into an area as an investigator, determine if something is wrong, and then use critical thinking skills to determine when something happened and why it happened? Auditing skills can make you the "Sherlock Holmes" of the manufacturing and service sectors. Auditing as a skill is both needed and useful. It is also a valued profession with roots going back to the 1930s.

The modern era of auditing started in the 1930s as a means of government accountancy, then moved into the corporate financial arena as a means of monitoring meant to inhibit the excesses that led in part to the Great Depression. Auditing later found its way into manufacturing where it evolved along with that industry.

Though founded in 1947, the International Organization for Standardization (ISO) really began to gain momentum during the 1980s with the beginning of worldwide recognition of the value of its standards. In its bellwether standard ISO 9001 as well as the industry-specific offshoots ISO 13485 (medical devices), AS9100 (aerospace), IATF 16949 (automotive), and ISO 14001 (environmental management), the existence of a robust audit program is mandated in order to verify conformance and effectiveness of an organization's quality or environmental management system. This mandate led to a surge in demand for those with auditing skills and the firm establishment of auditing as a profession. This change occurred along with the surge in prominence of both systems thinking and conformance auditing. Once the practical benefits of systems auditing were realized in the service and transactional industries in addition to manufacturing, auditing then fully expanded through the use of the many types of diverse audits that we encounter today. Despite the expansion of auditing into different and diverse arenas, tools and techniques still remain constant. Though the subject of the audit may vary and auditor qualifications may differ drastically depending on the type of audit, many of the tools and techniques remain the same regardless of the type of audit being performed. Now that we have seen where auditing has come from, let's talk a little bit about where auditing is headed.

Auditors from any industry must "learn the language of upper management" if they truly want to affect positive change throughout their environments. This is a challenge that was put forth by Allan Sayle at the 20th annual Audit Division conference in Reno, Nevada, in October 2011. He stated that if quality auditors wanted to remain relevant and keep from becoming marginalized, they needed to add new skills and credentials, and even more importantly, move beyond conformance monitoring to determine how their work might impact the corporate bottom line. The purpose of this book is to accept that challenge in presenting two ways that auditors can "learn [to speak] the language of upper management"—either by helping to drive continuous improvement or by helping to manage risk.

A robust audit program can be thought of as a three-legged stool with the program platform resting on its three legs of conformance, risk management, and continuous improvement. The three components exist in every audit program, but the relative importance of each leg varies according to (1) organizational goals and objectives or (2) the maturity of the quality management system that the audit program is monitoring. The corrective action process, one of the outputs of an audit, is itself a type of continuous improvement. By identifying the root cause of an issue and removing it through corrective action, the overall organization becomes stronger as one systemic or chronic weakness is removed. The audit program responds to perceived risk by adjusting schedules, sample size, team composition, and so forth according to perceived risk. It helps an organization manage risk by monitoring processes, identifying risks, and verifying the effectiveness of corrective and preventive actions.

So if this is what is done now, what is the next step?

Lean is a way of approaching continuous improvement by eliminating process wastes, and has methods and tools that work well in concert with auditing tools and methods. Lean tools can be integrated into current audit methodology in order to develop a more robust, value-added, and continuous improvement-driving internal audit program. Accomplishing this integration will allow lean tools to give auditors the ability to drill deeper and wider in looking for weaknesses in business systems, in addition to nonconformance to the existing quality management system.

Risk management, the next "leg" of the "stool," can be more fully integrated into the audit program by learning to identify risk, by classifying findings according to risk, and by using risk-based thinking when making decisions. Auditors can and should directly audit the risk management program. They should also be given specific risk-related training.

Data and trend analysis can have a direct impact on a company's bottom line. It is incumbent on auditors to acquire these skills and to know how to incorporate them into the audit process. (See Chapter 4 and the Appendix.) This is true for both conformance and continuous improvement auditing.

Too often auditors are thought of like police officers (or enforcers), punishing bad behavior (nonconformances) by giving out tickets (audit findings). This perception can lead to antagonistic behaviors between the quality audit and other functions within an organization. This kind of behavior can undermine an organization's efforts to meet its goals and objectives. Expanding on the police (or peace) officer analogy, the ideal scenario acknowledges that while writing tickets (audit findings) is certainly part of the job, equally if not more important are the duties to serve (continuous improvement) and protect (risk management) the organization and all within it.

This book is about advancing the profession of auditing, as well as the skills of individual auditors. It is not meant to be a panacea: the one prescription to apply to an ailing body of knowledge. Rather, it is meant to be the start of a discussion. Do join the discussion in shaping this proud profession as we look ahead to the future.

1

Traditional Audits

Before we talk about *advanced* quality auditing, let's first look at how to conduct a *good* audit using traditional methods. There are many different types of audits; however, for the purposes of this book, we will look at process audits, quality management system (QMS) audits, and elemental audits. These three audit types, the most commonly used, are interrelated and arguably are the most impactful. As mentioned during the Introduction, comprehensive audit programs have elements of conformance, continuous improvement, and risk management with the emphasis shifting based on organizational goals and the maturity of the quality management system. Similarly, individual audits will have primary and secondary benefits.

A *process audit* is an assessment of an individual process for effectiveness and efficiency. Conformance to procedure is also assessed during a process audit, due to the understanding that a process that is not being implemented according to planned and documented practices would be, by default, less effective and efficient in the long run. Thus the primary focus of a process audit is to determine effectiveness and efficiency. The secondary focus is to verify conformance to established method.

A *systems audit* is an audit of organizational processes and their interrelationships. Conducting systems audits are a good way for an auditor to learn how an organization functions. As one might expect, since a systems audit is an audit of processes and their interrelationships, a QMS audit has the primary purpose of assessing the effectiveness of the quality management system.

An *elemental* or *clause audit* is the auditing for conformance of aspects of the QMS against elements or paragraphs of an ISO or other standard. When systems and elemental audits are combined to assess a quality management system, then both effectiveness and conformance are assessed. QMS audits are most commonly thought of as being done by ISO-accredited certification bodies (also called registrars) and ISO 9001,

ISO 13485, ISO 14001, AS9100, and ISO/TS 16949 registrants to assess the effectiveness of the QMS. However, it should be noted that QMS audits can be conducted to review any quality management system, not just those registered to ISO standards.

WHAT MAKES A GOOD AUDIT?

Before beginning any audit you must have some criteria to audit against. Otherwise, you have a walkthrough followed by the presentation of a bunch of opinions. Criteria can be conformance to requirements, attainment of project milestones, improvement initiative results, keeping up with a timeline, etc. Audit criteria typically come from one of four sources. In order of precedence they are: legal/regulatory, customer contracts, standards such as ISO, and organizational policies/ procedures/project milestones. If two requirements contradict one another, then the higher-level requirement takes precedence. One easy way to remember the sources of audit criteria is to think of the acronym L.O.C. k S. as shown in Figure 1.1.

   Note: Remember that when referring to the acronym, the criteria are not in order of precedence but rather are ordered in the way that is the most easy to remember.

   Audit criteria can be categorized into two categories of standards to audit against.

   Reference standards are external documents such as regulations, contracts, and ISO standards that establish minimum requirements—the L, C, and S of the L.O.C. k S. acronym.

   Performance standards are internal documents such as SOPs, work instructions, drawings, and other similar documents that describe *how* requirements will be met and that personnel performance must be audited against—the O of the L.O.C. k S. acronym.

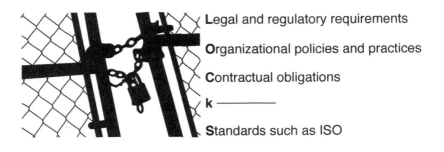

Legal and regulatory requirements

Organizational policies and practices

Contractual obligations

k ———

Standards such as ISO

Figure 1.1 L.O.C. k S.

Thanks to Larry Whittington of Whittington & Associates LLC for coming up with this clever acronym.

QMS AUDITING

When conducting an audit, the auditor should first assess the company documentation against the related reference documents. Any findings would then be against company documentation or the quality management system. Then the auditor should match employee actions and records (performance) against what is stated in their own internal documentation. Any findings noted would be against performance of actions as required. A memory aid and visual depiction of this process is seen in the *W* Factor illustration in Figure 1.2 developed by Erik V. Myhrberg PhD, along with a sample checklist template on the following pages.

In other words, if during the documentation review, a performance standard is found to be missing or in violation of a reference standard, then a nonconformance is written against the reference standard (left *valley* of the *W*). If observed actions aren't as documented, then a nonconformance is written against the internal document or performance standard (shown in the right *valley* of the *W*). This methodology avoids the confusion of citing multiple sources when referencing a single nonconformance. By having a structured, internal audit program with trained auditors and regularly scheduled audits, an organization can verify that it is working in a manner that will produce a product or service that meets customer needs and expectations.

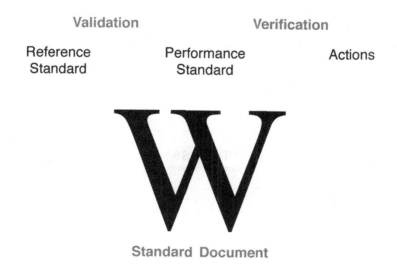

Figure 1.2 The *W* Factor.

Thanks to Erik V. Myhrberg, PhD of Moorhill International.

When citing a finding, the standard number, revision, and paragraph should be noted and the requirement stated on the audit documentation. Next, the witnessed condition is documented and conclusions drawn (major finding, minor finding, opportunity).

PROCESS AUDITING

A process can be thought of as an activity that turns inputs into outputs. One way to categorize inputs is the 6Ms: man, machine, material, method, measurement, and Mother Nature (the work environment), as shown in Figure 1.3. These categories can be used as a way to sort any possible thing that could impact a process. Process outputs could be a product (part or service), records or some type of signal, or a combination of these things, depending on the process.

The goals of a process audit are to verify that inputs are correct, assess how the process is performing, and confirm that outputs are as expected. Conformance with related instructions and procedures will also be verified. As with other audits, a process audit starts with planning. Prior to beginning the execution phase of the audit and going to the process location, auditors will want to compare work instructions and/ or standard operating procedures against related reference documents to confirm correct call outs for:

- Equipment settings (inputs)
- Raw material, components, subassemblies, actions, work instructions (inputs)
- Validated state (equipment set up) (input)
- Inspection, test or other type of monitoring (process performance)
- Product, records, signals (output)

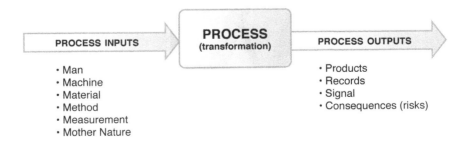

Figure 1.3 Process map.

The best way to approach a process audit is to look at the process being audited as a set of components—inputs, process performance, and outputs.

Looking at process inputs from the perspective of the 6Ms you can develop questions around each of the Ms. These questions are just a sampling of the possible questions that could be asked and may certainly be modified or expanded:

- Man
  - Does operator demonstrate competence in the operation?
  - Operator training records available?
- Machine
  - Equipment calibrated?
  - Equipment correct?
  - Equipment setup matches validated state?
- Method
  - Operator actions match instructions?
  - Instructions current revisions?
  - Instructions correct?
- Material
  - Correct materials?
  - Materials not defective?
- Measurement
  - Correct data being captured?
  - Data capture done correctly?
- Mother Nature
  - Environmental condition requirements met?
  - Environment monitored if required?
  - Safety and cleanliness evaluated?

Next, reviewing the process itself, you will assess process performance and process monitoring. Some questions to ask include:

- Performance
  - Performing as expected?
- Monitoring
  - Monitored as required?
  - Data recorded as required?
  - Data trending appropriately?

As stated above, process outputs will consist of the deliverable product or service, related records including statistical data and charts, alert or status signals, and finally any expected or unexpected consequences. Process output-related questions can include the following:

- Products
  - Does the product meet specified requirements?
  - Yields as expected?
  - Yields comparable to similar processes?
- Records
  - All required available?
  - Completely filled out?
  - Correctly filled out?
  - Good documentation practices followed per company procedure?
- Signals
  - Alerts, alarms, status signals sent as required?
- Consequences (risks)
  - Any expected or unexpected consequences?

Also, during the process audit the following documentation checks should be accomplished:

- Correct document(s) revised
- Forms correctly filled out
- Instructions match operator actions
- No uncontrolled documents at workstation verified

If the answer to any of the above questions is "I don't know," then further investigation is warranted. The next question that the auditor should ask is "Why don't we know?" There may very well be a valid reason for not having certain information or certain requirements; however, inquiries should be made regarding the absence of such information.

CONDUCTING THE AUDIT

The audit starts with the opening meeting. During the opening meeting, the audit team is introduced, the audit planned is reviewed, and audit criteria is confirmed. At this time any logistical needs are also addressed such as auditor meeting room, computer access, directions to the site, and so forth.

While conducting the audit, the auditor must always remember that they are a *guest* in the company, department, and area of the auditee, and as such must be polite and observant of existing rules of conduct. Audit (or objective) evidence will be collected during the audit, which the auditor will use to draw conclusions relating to auditee conformance, risks, or opportunities. At the close of each audit day, a summary of the audit findings (negative, positive, or undetermined) is presented to the auditee.

Audit evidence falls into one of four categories: documents, observations, records, and statements. One easy way to remember the types of audit evidence is to think of the acronym D. O. o R. S. as visualized in Figure 1.4 below.

Documents or documented information are organizational policies, standard operating, work instructions, drawings, and anything that provides guidance. Observations are those activities witnessed by the auditor. Records are completed forms maintained to provide a historical

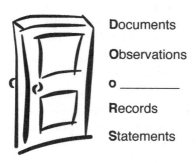

Documents

Observations

o _____

Records

Statements

Figure 1.4 D. O. o R. S.

Thanks to Larry Whittington of Whittington & Associates LLC for coming up with this clever acronym.

record of organizational activities. (Documents and records will now be referred to as documented information within ISO 9001:2015.) Statements run the gamut from interview question responses, explanations of activities, or overheard conversations.

Upon conclusion of the audit, a closing meeting is held. During that meeting, any findings will be presented along with their classifications. Reporting protocol and any required responses to findings will also be discussed, along with what remaining steps are required to close the audit.

The audit will be closed and reported according to either organizational procedures or directions from the individual client who commissioned the audit. Table 1.1 is an audit checklist template that could be used for system, element, or process audits. Once again, the practices explored in this section are by no means meant to be exhaustive. However, using these tools and methods will allow an auditor to conduct a comprehensive, professional, and successful audit. For a more exhaustive study on how to conduct a variety of audits, I would recommend the *The ASQ Auditing Handbook, Fourth Edition.*

Supplier Auditing

So what is the difference between conducting first-party (internal) and second-party (supplier) audits? The methodology is pretty much the same, but a lot else is different. Four important things that the supplier auditor needs to be aware of and prepare for the possibility of working around are:

Less transparency—Typically when auditing a supplier, you will only have the ability to witness supplier employees working on your job and review records solely from your jobs. The auditee will be less likely to volunteer areas of weakness or concern with their quality management system (QMS).

Less knowledge—You don't know as much about your supplier as you do about your own company regarding where problems are likely to occur and what *normal* behavior looks like.

Less access—You may not have access to certain areas or records due to proprietary information or other concerns.

Less authority—During internal audits, corporate values, history, and outlook shared by employees of the company being audited will often lead to agreement in a finding of nonconformance in those gray areas where there is not a clear requirement violation to cite. Suppliers are often evaluated in part by their performance during audits and will vigorously defend against a finding of nonconformance that cannot be tied back to a specifically stated requirement.

Table 1.1 Audit checklist template.

	Organization Improvement Project Q1 2015		
REQUIREMENT/ GOAL	**QUESTION**	**OBJECTIVE EVIDENCE**	**COMMENTS (Indicate Major, Minor or Opportunity)**
	☐ Y ☐ N ☐ NA		
	☐ Y ☐ N ☐ NA		
	☐ Y ☐ N ☐ NA		
	General Observations: ☐ Y ☐ N ☐ NA		

AUDIT CLOSURE

With limited time, limited resources, and additional challenges, one way to go about conducting an effective supplier audit is to remember that you are there to confirm the 4Cs: capability, controls, compliance, and customer focus.

One of the most important things is to ensure that the supplier remains capable of producing the product to specification. You audit this by reviewing validation reports, statistical process control, and training. Next, controls must be in place to quickly respond to both out-of-control and out-of-specification scenarios. This can be verified through review of the process monitoring, test, inspection, and internal audit programs. Compliance to applicable government regulations, ISO standards, and contracts may be addressed by the elemental approach to auditing.

Lastly, a supplier must be responsive to not only supplier corrective action requests and formal complaints, but also concerns, questions, and other requests for information. How quickly and thoroughly are supplier corrective action requests, formal complaints, and audit findings responded to? How are concerns, questions, and requests for information captured by the supplier and responded to? Are previously implemented corrective actions both in place and still effective?

Remember that the audit process is to be a benefit to the supplier as well as the customer. We already know that findings of noncompliance and opportunities for improvement, along with the related corrective actions, are part of an organization's continuous improvement process. How else might audits provide value to the supplier?

Best practices   Sharing of best practices related to some of the concerns that the supplier has that have been identified during the audit. Be careful with this, though, because as an external (to the supplier) auditor you don't want to suggest or imply corrective actions.

Taking back what your organization can do better   Many times some of the problems that suppliers have are caused or at least facilitated by their customers. If the supplier needs more information, better communication, or more responsiveness to questions from your organization, document these concerns and forward them to the appropriate parties upon your return to the office.

Supplier development   Some companies have Lean-Six Sigma and other training programs where key suppliers can send staff to participate. Auditors should be aware of and share information about these supplier development opportunities. Setting requirements for the minimum information needed as a response to corrective action requests or formal complaints, in the form of a template, can be of benefit to suppliers with a less developed quality management system.

Pitfalls to Avoid

Besides showing professionalism and politeness, it is important when conducting a supplier audit to follow site safety, gowning, and other rules. It also requires reasonableness when classifying findings. There should be flexibility and discussion allowed with any finding that does not have a specific and concrete requirement attached.

Another pitfall to be avoided is only looking at previous audit reports when planning for the audit. Other sources of information would be supplier corrective action request (SCAR) history, on-time delivery records, and receiving inspection records. If multiple sites use the supplier, contact the quality or supply chain personnel at those other sites to see if they have any concerns that you can address during your audit.

Conducting a successful supplier audit requires taking into account those challenges unique to supplier auditing. It is important to review the broadest cross section of data that is available when preparing for the audit, as well as being thorough while remembering you're not only the customer but also a guest of your supplier.

2

Lean Auditing for
Business Improvement

Taking a Lean Journey down the Audit Trail

INTRODUCTION TO LEAN PRINCIPLES

So what *exactly* is lean?

With roots dating back to the turn of the 20th century in this country, lean as we know it today is based on the Toyota Production System developed in the 1950s and used in tens of thousands of organizations across the world in the last 60 years. Lean is a set of management practices that organizations utilize to improve efficiency and effectiveness. Lean utilizes a set of methodologies and tools to identify and eliminate non-value-adding activities and waste from an organization's processes. Waste can be thought of an activity or situation that consumes resources but provides no value from the perspective of the customer. In other words, through implementation of lean methodologies, companies can do more work in less time with less cost. A byproduct of this increased efficiency is a reduction in process cycle time and eventually in an organization's product or service delivery lead time.

This improvement is accomplished by identifying and reducing operational waste, but not just any wastes—eight specific ones. The first seven lean wastes were identified as part of the Toyota Production System while the eighth was recognized some time later in the 1980s. Auditors should be aware that waste can exist not only within the work environment but also within the audit process itself. The eight wastes are:

1. **Waiting:** Time is money. Waiting ties up resources that could be more profitably engaged, such as a person that could be doing something else.

    • Example: In the work environment

    A job that is on hold or employees waiting around because paperwork is incomplete or a needed material/component is missing.

    • Example: During the audit

    Waiting while the assigned escorts to excuse themselves to do something else; waiting for requested records to be provided.

2. **Inventory:** While it is, of course, necessary to have enough inventory to "wet the line" when production of product (initiation of service) begins and reordering can be accomplished, having an overabundance of inventory that could potentially expire, be lost, or become damaged through excessive handling or movement is a form of waste.

    • Example: In the work environment

    Producing inventory in anticipation of an upcoming order while there is a lull in production might seem like a good idea at the time. Producing to a schedule based on financial forecast may also seem like a good idea. However, this inventory takes up space and may have to be moved around (and potentially damaged). It also represents assets that you can't do anything else with other than wait for the order to come. This is often referred to as *opportunity cost.*

    • Example: During the audit

    Requesting more records than you could reasonable expect to review.

3. **Defects:** The cost of catching and correcting errors, as well as, replacement of items or materials and possible reduced value to the customer, are all part of the waste of defects. It should also be noted that the farther downstream (closer to the last process step) this waste is caught, the more costly it becomes.

    • Example: In the work environment

    Defective parts, improperly completed forms, customer returns.

    • Example: During the audit

    Incorrectly citing something as a nonconformance before reviewing all of the evidence or incorrectly interpreting the audit criteria.

4. **Transportation:** Unnecessary conveyance (movement between locations) takes up time and energy and can lead to other forms of waste.

   - Example: In the work environment

     Having to move one pallet of material to access another that contains what is needed.

   - Example: During the audit

     Transport of requesting records or other objective evidence that in the end were not needed.

5. **Motion:** Having an inefficient workspace or having to move unnecessarily to complete a job is considered a form of waste because it can lead to lost time, hinder communication, impede effectiveness, and worst of all, potentially lead to injury.

   - Example: In the work environment

     Having to go to another room to pick up a printed document or form.

   - Example: During the audit

     Having to go back to an area that was previously visited due to poor audit planning.

   - Example: In the work environment

     Every time you have to move something to get to something else at your work station. Having to stretch, reach, or bend into a less than optimal position in order to complete an action (poor ergonomics). This waste can also occur while preparing the audit report.

6. **Overproduction:** Producing a product or service that cannot be delivered when complete is itself a form of waste. This inventory represents time, materials, and other resources that have been invested that cannot be compensated for while undelivered. The ideal scenario to work towards is to produce and deliver a product or service just as the customer is requesting it. This is perhaps the most insidious of the eight wastes because it so easily leads to other wastes.

   - Example: In the work environment

     Making more than is needed by the next process at any given time.

   - Example: During the audit

     An overly wordy audit report containing superfluous information.

7. **Excess processing:** Excess processing has two components: (1) taking actions that are more than are required and (2) taking actions that bring no additional value to the end customer.

   - Example: In the work environment

     Having two plastic liners for parts where only one is required. Maintaining a higher than mandated acceptable quality level (AQL) level when data shows that it could be lowered.

   - Example: During the audit

     Inappropriately large sample sizes. Spending too much time in one area.

8. **Non-utilization:** Not utilizing each employee up to full potential, thus sub-optimizing overall organizational effectiveness and possibly contributing to low employee morale.

   - Example: In the work environment

     Bringing in an outside consultant to do specialized training that internal resources could provide.

   - Example: In the work environment

     Having a lean team make improvements without allowing the area workers provide input.

   - Example: During the audit

     Lead auditor not delegating enough responsibility to other members of the audit team.

As a way to remember the different types of waste, you can take the first letter of each waste and rearrange them to spell DOWNTIME.

Now after the process owner and the process stakeholders, who better than an auditor to identify waste in an operation? The auditor is also uniquely suited to identify best practices that might be transferable across departments, functions, or even different locations.

If we are going to continue talking about waste, however, we must also look at defining the concept of value. Value must come from the customer's perspective. If the customer is willing to pay for something, then it has value. Think of the customer/supplier relationship as a person looking at a black box. The customer inputs an order along with payment and expects as output a good or service that meets their requirements, lasts as expected, and is delivered on time, at the desired cost. The customer really doesn't care what goes on inside the black box (what the supplier needs to do) to make that happen.

An example of a value-adding step in manufacturing is soldering a needed component onto a circuit board. Without the component, the board would not function and thus would have no value to the customer. Final inspection of the circuit board prior to shipping would be considered a non-value adding step since it does not add anything to the finished product (though it would possibly catch the defect of a missing component). The inspection should still be considered important as it helps keep defective merchandise from getting to the customer, yet it is non-value added (though necessary) because as an individual line item, the customer would not be willing to pay for it. After all, they are purchasing a circuit board (and what it does) and not an inspection service. The inspection would be considered a cost of doing business that the supplier factors into pricing.

PLAN-DO-CHECK-ACT (PDCA)

The PDCA process that is embedded within lean implementation has a natural application within the audit process as well. The activities taking place during each phase of this cycle are:

PLAN

- Confirm purpose, scope, and authority to begin
- Determine measurement for success and set targets
- Develop implementation plan
- Establish reporting and communication protocols

DO

- Implement plan
- Record results

CHECK

- Compare actual versus expected results
- Document
- Perform root cause analysis if necessary

ACT

- Standardize corrective, preventive, or improvement action
- Issue report
- Implement corrective action if necessary

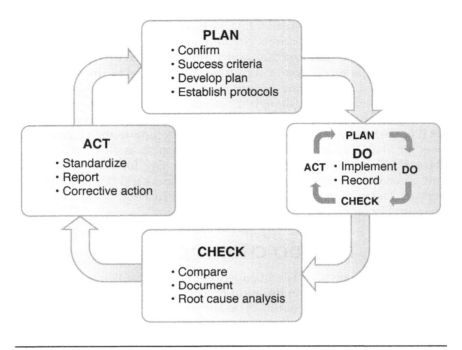

Figure 2.1 PDCA cycle.

The cycle is repeated until the desired result is achieved. The process works the same whether managing an overall program or for an individual project or audit, and is outlined in Figure 2.1. The smaller PDCA cycle in the DO box represents going through the process for an individual audit or project.

INTEGRATING LEAN TOOLS INTO THE AUDIT PROGRAM

There are specific tools in the lean toolbox that lend themselves well to use by auditors as a part of continual improvement efforts to eliminate waste and improve processes. Let's take a look at just a couple of them.

Value stream mapping (VSM)   When conducting a quality audit, it is customary to process map or flowchart the process in preparation then, (1) match documents and procedures to regulations/standards, (2) match employee actions to internal documents/procedures, and (3) verify appropriate training, operating controls, environmental controls and record keeping, as a minimum. Additionally, an auditor might look to identify best practices as well as opportunities for improvement.

Incorporating VSM into an audit adds another level of analysis. Which actions are value-add and which are not? Are value-add actions optimized while non-value-add actions minimized? How efficient are the feeder value streams that flow into the primary value stream that is being audited? Where are the potential bottlenecks in the value stream flow? What are the process yields? What are the feedback loops in place to monitor and evaluate the effectiveness of the system under review? How close are we to matching product cycle time to *takt* (consumer consumption rate) time? All of this allows us to identify waste in our system, while providing for a more robust process review. See Case in Point 2.1 later in this chapter for an example of this distinction drawn from an actual audit.

SIPOC (supplier-inputs-process-outputs-customers) diagrams These allow for a more expansive analysis of overall work flow than the traditional flowcharting or process mapping done during audits. Knowing where inputs come from (what shift, what production line, which supplier and so forth) is as valuable in looking for trends and determining root cause as is knowing what the process inputs are or should be. Knowing not just the expected process outputs, but also the customer for those outputs, provides insight into whether or not requirements meet end user needs and expectations. In other words, getting all of the outputs that are expected does not always guarantee that the item produced will function as desired by the end user.

One simple example of this would be a bolt that meets the related ANSI specification for thread width and pitch, but on occasion might not screw into its mating part. One way to address this issue might be to tighten tolerances of one or both parts once this issue is discovered. In a case like this, the auditor might ask the question, does meeting specification = meeting functional needs? By matching process outputs to customer (internal or external) needs and expectations we can often identify unforeseen improvement opportunities and thereby provide additional value to our customers.

CONSTRUCTING A LEAN AUDIT CHECKLIST USING THE AUDIT CHECKLIST DEVELOPMENT MATRIX

Auditors can use the audit checklist development matrix (ACDM) shown in Figure 2.2 to construct a customized audit checklist dependent upon the purpose of the audit. The matrix is my variation of the Portable Universal Quality Lean (PUQL) Audit Model template developed by Janet Bautista-Smith and first presented in *Auditing Beyond Compliance* (Quality Press, 2012).

System Evaluation (Validation)						Continuous Improvement
		Performance Verification				
Reference Document Paragraph	Reference Standard Requirement	Reference Standard Paragraphs	Standard Observation Interviews	Records	Positive Practices Opportunities	Lean Auditing
1. Government regulation 2. ISO Standard 3. Contract 4. Purchase Order	1. State the requirement 2. Any related findings from most recent audit?	1. What is the requirement? 2. What do our documents say? 3. Do required documents exist?	1. Do we do what we said we would? 2. Are employees effectively trained? 3. Working environment safe and clean? 4. Work environment suitable for operations? 5. Are adequate resources provided to achieve goals?	1. Are required records available? 2. Are records complete and accurate? 3. Are records consistently filled out? 4. Are good documentation practices followed?	1. Any positive practices that may be transferred to other operations? 2. Any opportunities for improvement?	1. Is the process yield as expected? 2. How does the process yield compare to similar processes? 3. Any identified wastes? 4. Any non-value-add steps? 5. Can cycle time be reduced?
A	B	C	D	E	F	G

Figure 2.2 Audit checklist development matrix (ACDM).

To use the ACDM, each individual criterion should have its own row in columns *A* and *B*. Then specific questions should be formulated from the questions found in column *C* and based on the related performance standards (standard operating procedures, work instructions, drawings, and so forth). This is all done during the audit planning phase along with determining a sampling plan. The questions in columns *D* through *F* will be asked during the implementation phase of the audit.

Initial supplier assessment would just follow columns *A* through *C* of the ACDM. A systems audit would follow columns *A* through *F*. A process audit would follow columns *C* through *F*. The lean audit described in column *G* could be done as a solo audit or added on to any one of the preceding audits seamlessly. A template for your use is provided.

By taking a lean approach to auditing, auditors can identify process waste at the same time as looking for nonconformance. This can be done seamlessly without having to do "separate but equal" conformance and improvement auditing. Lean auditing will lead to increased effectiveness of the audit program as often responses to audit findings will not stop at just correction and prevention, but also actively seek to improve the process under review. Lean auditing will also lead to greater visibility of the audit program among upper management by allowing for more opportunities to positively impact the company bottom line. In conclusion, combining lean and audit methodology will greatly expand the versatility and effectiveness of the audit process, and its impact on the bottom line.

CASE IN POINT 2.1: LEAN RECEIVING AUDIT

So let's compare auditing a medical device company's receiving process in a more traditional conformance driven manner versus auditing by blending in lean methodology. For less complex processes, I always like to start off by imagining what activities must take place based on my own experiences with similar areas, drawing a flowchart of activities without reading any procedures and then asking what questions remain. Similarly I leave the decision blocks incomplete until I know the reaction to a given scenario. See Figure 2.3.

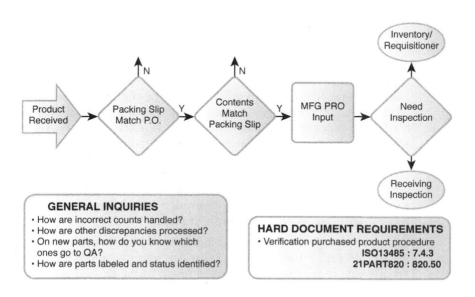

Figure 2.3 Receiving process flowchart.

The term *hard document requirements* refers to those documented procedures required by ISO 13485:2003 (the most current version at the time the audit where this flowchart was used took place). The next step is to read the relevant standard operating procedures and work instructions to provide more detail. This is my preferred method because brainstorming beforehand what questions need be asked and what actions accounted for highlights opportunities in the system if those questions aren't answered once the work instructions and standard operating procedures have been read and the flowchart details filled in.

Once the relevant documents are reviewed, as a minimum the following questions must be asked in order to assure conformance with requirements:

- What is the requirement?
- What do our documents say?
- Do we do what we said we would do?
- Are our records complete and consistently filled out from one record to the next?

When we incorporate lean thought into our audit process, we start to look at where value is found in the process being audited.

Value-add questions include:

- What is the value proposition? In other words is this process something that the customer would pay for? If not, the process should be eliminated if possible and streamlined if elimination is not possible. In the case of receiving inspection, while important from the standpoint of helping to manage the risk of defective material or components entering the manufacturing pipeline, it contains no value from the perspective of the customer. After all, "they are not buying an inspection service." Thus the receiving inspection process should be streamlined as much as can reasonably be done. This is accomplished by adjusting sampling levels based on the past quality history of a given supplier, and also by designating certain outstanding suppliers as dock-to-stock for certain products where those products don't go through receiving inspection at all but are sampled from inventory once or twice a year per organization procedures.

- What is the cycle time of this process? How long does this process take? Could it be done more quickly? Are resource allocations appropriate to the task? Is this metric even tracked?

- How efficient is this process? What is the yield for this process? How does it compare to expectations? To similar processes? One example of the yield for an inspection process might be the number of pieces inspected per hour (per person).

- What are the value-add and non-value-add steps? Can we eliminate, combine, or shorten any non-value-add process steps? Can we optimize value-add steps?

In order to visually depict value-add and non-value-add steps as well as cycle time, the value stream map shown in Figure 2.4 is a useful tool. A value stream map is a high-level process map that shows value-add, non-value-add, lead time, cycle time, and step/process yields. Using a value stream map in conjunction with a process map and a process flowchart allows a total capture of the activities in a given area.

The value stream map in Figure 2.4 looks at cycle and lead times, and also takes into account scheduling as well as the next step in manufacturing process—production. In a less mature quality management system, it is quite possible that the auditor, through value stream mapping, might be capturing this important information for the first time. By incorporating lean methodology into the audit process, in this case through the use of value stream mapping, we can now not only assess conformance but also begin to assess the effectiveness and efficiency of an existing process. Depending on the audit goals, an auditor might use a process flowchart, a value stream map, or both.

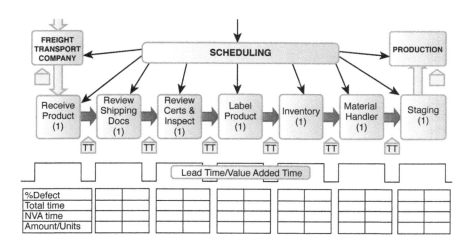

Figure 2.4 Receiving value stream map.

A 3PL/Logistics company (Company A) provides a warehousing service for a manufacturing company, Company Z. Company Z gives the orders to the Logistics/Warehousing company (Company A) for picking the materials from its warehouse and shipping directly to the customer. During the last three months, there has been a noticeable decline of the on-time delivery. During the audit of the process, there was no observable change in the process. Upon further evaluation of the process metrics by the lean audit team, it was noted that the material picking cycle time showed an increasing trend at the same timeline as the decreasing on time delivery. From these primary and secondary metrics, it was discovered that there was a recent change in the material packaging configuration triggered by the customer's material cost saving initiative. Ordering the materials in bulk versus standard pack was a cost savings for the customer, but resulted into longer picking time as this required counting of the materials per order. This scenario represents a classic example of sub-optimization: improvement of one aspect of a company at the expense of the performance of the whole. The lean auditing method, which included verification of measurement/metrics, led to the un-covering of this process change and an appropriate action plan.

i Thanks to Janet Bautista-Smith for sharing this anecdote from the logistics arena.

3

Risk-Based Quality Auditing (RBQA)[ii]

FOR WANT OF A NAIL...

To talk about risk-based quality auditing, we must first understand risk and how we manage it.

Overview

ISO 31000:2009 defines *risk* as the effect of uncertainty on objectives. ISO 14971:2007, used in the medical device industry, defines *risk* as the combination of the probability of occurrence of harm and the severity of that harm.

Manufacturers also recognize *consumer risk*—the risk of accepting a bad part as good (beta error)—and *producer risk*—the risk of rejecting a good part as bad (alpha error). Anecdotally, I tend to think of risk as opportunity for disaster (OFD).

WHAT IS RISK MANAGEMENT

A risk management program is a series of interrelated processes and tools designed to identify, describe, assess, mitigate, and track risk, thereby managing organizational risk. Industry has various types of tools to both identify and assess risk, such as failure mode and effects analysis (FMEA), fault tree analysis (FTA), and hazard analysis of critical control points (HACCP). Another commonly used tool is strengths-weaknesses-opportunities-threats (SWOT) analysis.

We also have the means for ranking risk that then allows us to prioritize how we allocate resources to deal with that risk. The most commonly used tools are the risk matrix and the risk priority number (RPN). Let's take a look at some brief definitions.

---

ii Training program © 2013 Lance Coleman and Duke Okes.

Risk Priority Number

Begin by ranking each of the following, on a scale of either 1 to 5 or 1 to 10, with one being best-case and 5 (or 10) being worst-case scenario:

- Likelihood of occurrence
- Severity of occurrence
- Likelihood of detection

$$RPN = likelihood \times severity \times mitigation$$

Failure Mode and Effects Analysis (FMEA)

FMEA is a risk matrix that contains the following elements:

- Process inputs
- Process outputs
- Risk assessment using RPN
- Risk mitigation measures
- Residual risk assessment using RPN

Fault Tree Analysis

While FMEA tries to identify all of the potential failure modes for a product or ways that it could fail, fault tree analysis tries to identify all of the ways that the process itself can fail.

Hazard Analysis of Critical Control Points (HACCP)

Hazard analysis of critical control points (HAACP) is a systematic preventive approach to food safety as well as biological, chemical, and physical hazards in a production process that may cause the finished good to be unsafe, and designs countermeasures to reduce these risks to a safe level.

Strengths-Weaknesses-Opportunities-Threats (SWOT) Analysis

This is a two by two matrix with strengths/weaknesses across the top x-axis and opportunities/threats on the y-axis, used as a planning aid.

The attempts to prevent risky events from occurring are called risk mitigation. The preferred hierarchy for risk mitigation is:

1. Design it out
2. Alarm when it occurs
3. Warnings (labeling) that risk-laden event could occur

After all efforts at risk mitigation have been implemented, a new risk assessment is performed and this new assessment value is considered the residual risk. At this point an organization must make the business decision of whether the benefits of going with a particular product or course of action outweigh the residual risk. A risk management plan is a living document that must be continually updated, and those updates responded to when necessary. Once risks have been assessed, potential causes identified, potential impacts contemplated, and mitigation strategies developed, a model is developed that includes residual risk. Every effort should be made to continually update the risk model to take into account data from the field, as well as ongoing production information.

Instilling Robustness

For a truly robust risk management program, the program should encompass all aspects of a product life cycle, from design to end-of-life disposal. This means that executive-level management must be involved from the start, in order to allocate the appropriate resources to collect the needed data as well as to develop and implement a robust risk management program. When teams are formed, they should be cross-functional in nature in order to model the broadest possible range of risks. Often in the medical device field our risk classifications are tied to the FDA classifications of mandatory reportable events tied to public safety, for example:

Critical—Likely to cause death or serious harm

Major—Not likely to cause death or serious harm, but may possibly cause injury

Moderate—Remote possibility that malfunction could cause injury

Minor—Highly unlikely to cause injury or harm

So what happens if, as a medical device component manufacturer, you don't have access to the data that would allow you to make the above determinations? Then you need to expand your risk classifications. After risk to public safety as discussed above, there are opportunities to categorize, plan for, and react to other types of risk. For example:

a. Product risk—nonfunctional, functional but out of dimensional tolerance, visual defect, documentation error and so on.

b. QMS risk—missing or faulty element that could lead to other issues, chronic problems, isolated incidents and so on (addressed by incorporating risk management into your internal audit program).

c. Business risk—cost of failed design of experiments (DOE) or other optimization initiatives. Cost of rejecting good part as bad.

By expanding the risk model to incorporate multiple categories of risk, a wider variety of potential failure modes can be identified and accounted for. Accounting for multiple types of risk also allows the risk management process to be more easily integrated with improvement efforts. Although I reference the medical device industry in this example of how to expand the risk model, this approach would be effective in any industry.

Pitfalls to Avoid

Now that we've covered the basics, let's look at some common pitfalls things that might not be so obvious at first blush:

1. Risk management not fully integrated with other systems (for example, control of nonconforming material, corrective and preventive action [CAPA] internal audit, and so on). By identifying and classifying various types of risk, the organization knows how respond to internal issues when they arise. One example might be when either a nonconforming material report or audit finding might initiate the generation of a CAPA based on a risk assessment using established criteria.

2. Risk management thought of as a set of tools and records rather than a comprehensive program. How often as an auditor have you asked about an auditee's risk management program and were given an FMEA log and records?

3. Risk management is an organic program that must reflect current conditions. There should be a continual feedback and adjustment loops in place. Risk assessments must be updated and controls adjusted, based on both internal and external data. Often there is no process in place to make this determination and implement changes when necessary.

4. Failure to assess any risks that might be associated with efforts to improve.

To summarize, risk management is a program that is not only required but has value well beyond that of meeting regulatory requirements. When implemented properly, the benefits of having a robust risk management program go beyond the realm of securing public safety and into the arena of protecting corporate health as well.

RISK ASSESSMENT

Risk assessment is an integral part of the risk management process that requires subject matter expertise, analytical skills, and interpersonal skills (to successfully work in a team). After a risk has been identified, the first step is to form a cross-functional team to assess the risk. Ideally,

Table 3.1 Risk matrix.

FREQUENCY	IMPACT			
	Neglibible	Minor	Major	Critical
Rarely				
Occasionally				
Frequently				
Continually				
Low Risk (L)		Medium Risk (M)		High Risk (H)

the team should include at least one member from quality who would most likely be a quality engineer (or in a small company possibly the quality manager) and one subject matter expert (SME) who is not a stakeholder. There should also be the broadest possible representations of disciplines so as to capture the broadest possibilities of potential risk.

Industry has various types of tools to identify, categorize, and assess risk. Failure mode and effects analysis (FMEA), strengths-weaknesses-opportunities-threats (SWOT) analysis, hazard analysis of critical control points (HACCP), decision trees, and risk matrices are just some of them. Table 3.1 is an example of a risk matrix that has impact of adverse event on one axis and likelihood of occurrence (or frequency) on the other. Color coding is used to rank criticality of the risk in this example. Different patterns could also be used to differentiate between levels or risk instead of colors.

Table 3.2 shows an excerpt from a risk assessment form where the risk matrix has built-in check boxes alongside a series of potential responses based on the level of risk.

A more refined approach for ranking and prioritizing risk is the risk priority number (RPN). The risk priority number provides more information upon which to base a decision than the risk matrix because, in addition to impact and frequency, the RPN takes into account the likelihood of detection once an adverse event has occurred. The RPN is determined by ranking each of the following, on a scale of usually 1 to 10 (though sometimes 1 to 5 may work better and is acceptable), with 1 being best-case and 10 being worst-case scenario:

- Likelihood of occurrence
- Severity of occurrence
- Likelihood of detection

Table 3.2 Risk assessment form risk matrix.

	IMPACT				Recommended Action
FREQUENCY	**Neglibible**	**Minor**	**Major**	**Critical**	☐ Initiate a product recall ☐ Open CAPA
Rarely	☐ M	☐ H	☐ H	☐ H	investigation ☐ Open complaint in
Occasionally	☐ L	☐ M	☐ H	☐ H	MasterControl (Approval required for
Frequently	☐ L	☐ M	☐ M	☐ H	below actions)
Continually	☐ L	☐ L	☐ M	☐ M	☐ Write NCMR and investigate
	Low Risk (L)	Medium Risk (M)	High Risk (H)		☐ Correct and document ☐ Track and trend

The rankings are then plugged into the following equation:

$$RPN = \text{likelihood} \times \text{severity} \times \text{mitigation}$$

The numbers are multiplied out to arrive at a final score or RPN.

Two other considerations that are often taken into account are organizational vulnerability to the event and rapidity of onset (how much time does the organization have to respond). Typically, rather than adding digits onto the RPN, a predetermined number is added on to the RPN for an adjusted score if either vulnerability to or rapidity of onset of an adverse event adds to organizational risk. It is up to the risk assessment team to determine what an acceptable level of risk is. It is also up to the risk assessment team at that point to identify and assess all of the different types of risk recognized by their organizational model.

To provide consistency of risk assessment, definitions of the different classifications must be clear, recognized and understood. Table 3.3 and Table 3.4 provide two examples of describing likelihood of occurrence.

Table 3.3 Likelihood of detection.

Frequency	Rarely	Occasionally	Frequently	Continually
Qualitative	Unlikely to occur again	Occurs once in a while	Occurs several times in the life of the product	Occurring continually
Quantitative	1 in 1,000 > 1 in 1,000,000	1 in 100 > 1 in 1,000	1 in 10 > 1 in 100	1 in 10 >

Table 3.4 Defining likelihood.

Likelihood of Detection	Highly Unlikely	Unlikely	Likely	Very Likely
Qualitative	Highly Unlikely	More likely than not to miss event	More likely than not to catch event	Very high probability of detection
Quantitative	Less than 10%	11%–50%	51%–84%	85% or better
Numerical Value	1–3	4–6	7–8	9–10

Table 3.5 Defining impact.

Impact	Negligible	Minor	Major	Critical
Consumer	There is no risk of injury to the patient and/or operator.	The potential problem could result in a non-serious injury to the patient and/or operator that does not require medical intervention.	The potential problem could result in a non-serious injury to the patient and/or operator that requires medical intervention.	The potential problem could result in death or serious injury to the patient and/or operator.
Product	Paperwork error.	May cause failure of part attributes.	May cause failure of part variables. Failure of attribute that could affect form fit or function.	May cause injury to operators, client or end user. May cause final product to fail in the field.
QMS	Improperly completed forms and records (Information still retrievable).	Violation of internal procedure or work instruction; Current practice that meets requirement is accurately documented.	Violation of customer requirements or internal requirement. Systemic or chronic failure of QMS requirement. Multiple related minor violations. Cause great harm to other operations in the company.	Noncompliance that is itself a hazard or may lead to hazardous condition. Direct violation of ISO standards or cGMP. Absence of required procedure or record.
Business	Minimal financial risk or risk of production delay due to change.	Possibility of production delays if change fails. Cost of materials in producing parts for inspection.	Potential damage to connected equipment. Failed change could lead to substantial financial risk due to the probability of extensive production delays and could potentially lead to customer loss.	Places company in immediate legal or product liability jeopardy.

Severity or impact might be defined as seen in Table 3.5.

After all efforts at risk mitigation have been implemented, a new RPN is determined using the same scale; this value is considered the residual risk. Then a decision is made as to whether the residual risk is acceptably low enough to move forward with the project. After the initial risk assessment is complete, informational feedback loops should be established to continue to collect data from both internal and external sources in order to confirm that the risk assessment remains accurate over time.

An FMEA as shown in Table 3.6 is a table constructed to easily show risk assessment for each step of the process using a RPN both before and after attempts at mitigation to either eliminate or reduce the risk. An auditor should understand how to interpret the FMEA as part of auditing project/program planning or even the risk management program itself.

Now that we've covered the basics, let's look at some common pitfalls often encountered during the risk assessment process that might not be so obvious at first blush:

1. Use of either quantitative (1 occurrence per 100 opportunities, 1 occurrence per 1000 opportunities and so on) or qualitative (rarely, occasionally, often) assessments solely for frequency of occurrence when there are times that a program may require one or the other, depending on the situation.

2. Risk management is an organic program that must reflect current conditions. There should be a continual feedback and adjustment loop in place. Risk assessments must be updated and controls adjusted, based on both internal and external data. Often there is no process in place to make this determination and implement changes when necessary.

Table 3.6 FMEA table.

FMEA Table: Pre-Mitigation								
Process Step/Input	Potential Failure Mode	Potential Failure Effects	S E V	Potential Causes	O C C	Current Controls	D E T	R P N

3. Context should be provided as a part of the risk assessment. In other words, are there external factors that may fluctuate, that could significantly increase risk? Examples might be rising oil prices, natural disasters, or a principle supplier of goods going out of business.

4. Be sure when looking at examples of potential adverse events that different members of the team are ranking them consistently. As this process is somewhat subjective, a difference between 5 and 6 as rated by two different assessors is acceptable. A difference in ranking between 4 and 7 is not, and so definitions would need to be clarified.

RISK MANAGEMENT INTEGRATION

Now let us consider how, for optimal effectiveness, the risk management program should be integrated with other quality systems such as:

- Customer complaints
- Process monitoring
- Internal audits
- External audits
- Material review board
- Corrective and preventive action

Integration is accomplished by embracing risk-based thinking. ISO 9001:2015 defines risk as the effect of uncertainty on an expected result. Risk-based thinking is looking at all aspects of an organization from organizational structure to business environment to resources needed to decisions made from the perspective of the risks involved. This includes past, current, and future state decision makings as seen in the following examples.

Past: Using risk assessment to categorize and determine the scope of adverse events that have occurred.

Current State: Looking at events that have occurred and using risk analysis to determine the correct response.

Future State: Doing cost-benefit-analysis to make a decision on a course of action. Embedding risk management into this process by making risk (of not succeeding or of making things worse) as part of the cost determination.

Integration is further accomplished by including a risk assessment as part of the evaluation process for each category of data. The data must then be sorted, reported to site management, and analyzed. For ISO-registered companies, it is mandated that risk management be one of the items reviewed as part of a regularly scheduled management review whose purpose is to evaluate the effectiveness of the quality management system. Adjustments to actions, improvements, and corrections must be made based on the analysis of data and conclusions drawn. There should be a continuous feedback loop to monitor processes and make adjustments as required. If necessary, systems should then be modified to address identified areas of concern. Prioritization of actions taken, and resources allocated to those actions, will be based on risk ranking.

As part of the planning process, it should be determined what the reporting protocols are and what triggers exist to let the organization know when to take action. There should also be triggers for when to initiate a risk assessment that may be related to safety, quality management systems, cost, or any other event deemed important by the organization. These triggers are the organizational control mechanisms that are designed to mitigate risk by lessening the likelihood of occurrence and/ or lessen the impact should an adverse event occur. Also to be addressed are what documentation is required and what records must be kept.

Planning should account for linkages throughout all phases of development and production. The risk assessment matrix may be integrated into existing forms, developed as its own form, or both. Training must be accomplished for all levels of the organization—not just on individual work instructions, but on the risk management system as a whole, and how it is supposed to function. General training on risk management principles—how they work and why we should care—is

Table 3.7 Sample auditor risk management training matrix.

Possible Risk Management Training Matrix for Auditors	Level 1	Level 2	Level 3
What is risk?	X		
How do we recognize it?	X		
How do we manage it?	X		
Risk management tools	X	X	
Auditing the risk management system	X	X	X
Incorporating risk evaluation into existing audits	X	X	X
Level 1—Basic understanding **Level 2**—Apply the principles **Level 3**—Ability to train others			

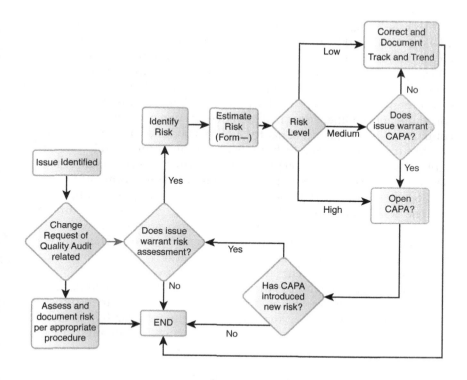

Figure 3.1 Risk identification and response process flow.

also important in order to ensure buy in amongst crucial stakeholders. A simple auditor risk management-training matrix is shown in Table 3.7. Figure 3.1 shows a sample adverse event identification and risk management process flowchart.

Three concerns are critical to the successful integration of risk management with other systems: effective communication, allocation of necessary resources, and thinking strategically by incorporating risk management into long term planning across all levels of the organization. When these three things happen, it becomes possible for the risk management program to be seamlessly integrated with the QMS and other organizational systems.

RISK-BASED QUALITY AUDITING

Risk elimination. Risk management. Risk mitigation. This is the language of upper management that we as auditors from any industry must learn if we truly want to effect positive change throughout our environment.

This is a challenge that was put forth by Allan Sayle, one of the keynotes at the 20th annual Audit Division conference in Reno, Nevada, held in October 2011. He stated that if quality auditors wanted to remain relevant and keep from becoming marginalized, they needed to add new skills and credentials, and even more importantly, move beyond conformance monitoring to determine how their work might impact the corporate bottom line. This can be achieved in two ways: either by driving continuous improvement (Chapter 2 of this book) or by managing risk. I would further state that a truly robust audit program, as stated earlier, is a three-legged stool with the program platform resting on its three legs of conformance, risk management, and continuous improvement.

So what does all this have to do with auditing? Actually, quite a bit. The four phases of auditing are planning, execution, closure, and reporting. During each phase of the auditing process, there is a risk assessment and risk management component, even when they are not recognized as such. So let's take a look at how risk assessment and management naturally occurs within the audit program.

First, though, let's discuss the hierarchy of risk. Every company must establish a hierarchy of risk as part of their risk management program. The following prioritization represents a common hierarchy but is by no means absolute or 100% consistent from company to company:

1. Safety

2. Functionality / intended use suitability

3. Out of specification—variable

4. Out of specification—attribute

5. Out of control process

6. Documentation issues

7. Reject good parts as bad

How this risk is assessed may also vary from industry to industry, company to company, or even from site to site within the same company.

During the planning phase of the audit program, decisions must be made as to what to audit, when to audit, and at what frequency to audit. Once you get beyond regulatory, standard and customer requirements, company exposure to risk is the driving factor in making these determinations. When planning an individual audit, audit focus and sampling level are determined by both historical data (when applicable) and risk exposure.

During the execution phase of an audit, determinations must be sometimes made on whether to stick with the original audit plan and schedule or pursue an area of concern that came up during the audit. The first determining factor in how to proceed is if there is an immediate safety concern, then secondly whether or not the issue or concern falls under the scope of the audit. The third consideration would be the level of risk that exists if the concern were not to be further explored. Another risk-based decision is made when determining whether or not to increase sample size based on what the auditor is seeing from the initial sample.

Classification of findings, determination of acceptable corrective actions, effectiveness, verification, and timeframes for action all have an element of risk assessment included. Lastly, whether to schedule a follow-up audit upon audit closure is just one more decision that is made based on risk to the company, customer, or public.

So if we are already doing all of this risk assessing and managing naturally as part of a robust audit program, what is the point of this chapter? Well, we as quality professionals *know* that having method and structure to a process is a better way to achieve consistently positive results than letting things happen organically.

Now, we will talk about how to more formally integrate risk management into an audit program. First of all, risk-based quality auditing can be thought to occur within three levels of organizational maturity:

> **Level 1**—Planning and reporting based on risk; this is what is typically going to occur naturally within most audit programs.

> **Level 2**—Evaluating how well risk management is incorporated into individual quality management system processes.

> **Level 3**—Determining enterprise-level risks relating to quality management system processes.

Maturity of the QMS will usually determine what level of risk management an organization is implementing. Three concrete things can be done to formally integrate risk management into the internal audit process:

1. Changes to the baseline annual audit plan should be made based on areas of concern or opportunity identified in the annual senior management meeting, and by the use of a risk-based methodology.

2. Definitions and methodology for classifying audit findings should reflect a previously determined risk assessment matrix.

3. Reporting results and recommending action based on audit findings should reflect the assessment of risk as determined during the audit process. See Table 3.8 for one example.

These three suggestions provide a good starting foundation for formally integrating risk management into your internal audit program. RBQA can be conducted as stand-alone audits or as part of an existing audit. RBQA can review aspects of the quality management system or the risk management program itself.

Table 3.8 Finding classification by risk.

Minor	Major	Critical
Violation of internal procedure or work instruction. Current practice that meets requirement is not accurately documented. Could lead to failure of part attributes.	Violation of customer requirement or internal requirement. Systemic or chronic failure of QMS requirement. Multiple related minor violations. Issue that could lead to failure of either part function or part variables. Ethical violations. Or issues that could cause great harm to other operations.	Noncompliance that is itself a hazard or may lead to hazardous condition. Direct violation of ISO standards or cGMP. Issue that could directly lead to field failure of finished good. Legal violations. Lost required record or procedure. Zero documented evidence of compliance.

One thorough process to conduct a risk-based quality audit is to use the Risk is the Compass model developed by Denis Devos, a career auditor and ASQ Fellow. A process must do more than simply comply with a set of requirements; a process must be effective. As auditors, it must be our role to audit beyond compliance and to evaluate the effectiveness of a process. By one measure, an effective process is one that is robust to risk. No matter what happens, the process will yield a successful outcome. Therefore, an auditor should evaluate how well a process manages risks to the process as a strong indicator of its overall effectiveness. In the Risk is the Compass model, a process flowchart is created and then risks to the process steps are listed along with any corresponding *enablers* that may be in place to mitigate those risks. Enablers (or controls) are simply any aspect of a process that has been designed in order to *enable* the process to be successful. Examples include properly trained personnel, proper materials, workspace lighting, clear work instructions, tools and inspection devices, and so on that are brought to bear to ensure successful execution of the process. Process risks are those aspects of the process that inhibit success. If one were driving to work, there are characteristic risks associated with the process such as getting into an accident, heavy traffic, construction, bad weather, and so on that can inhibit getting to work on time. When an auditor is preparing for an audit, he or she can list the enablers and risks next to each process step as shown in Figure 3.2. Then the next step is for the auditor to create a set of audit questions that investigate how well the enablers and risks balance each other. It is hoped that there is a sufficient level of control for each of the risks in the process. If there are too many enablers in place for the risk (such as too much product inspection), then an auditor could conclude that the process is over-controlled, resulting in wasted resources. If, on the other hand, the auditor finds evidence that enablers or controls are insufficient to manage a certain process risk, then the auditor has the basis for a finding that the

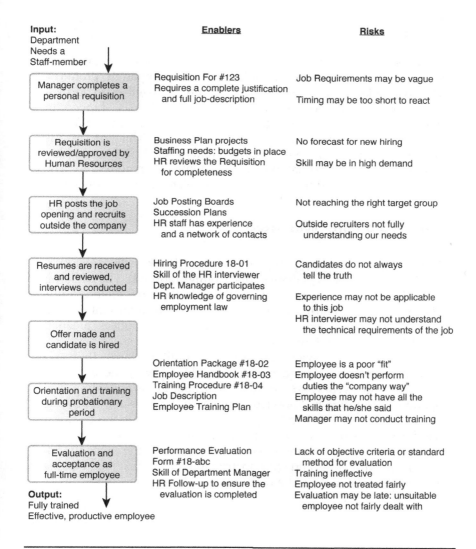

Figure 3.2 Hiring process map showing enablers and risks[iii].

iii Denis Devos, *Risk is the Compass*™ (2006 ASQ World Conference on Quality and Improvement, ASQ Audit Division Newsletter, May 2014)

process is under-controlled, and improvement is needed. Therefore, audit questions now become more than simply check-in-the-box compliance questions, but move into the realm of real process evaluation.

CASE IN POINT 3.1: AUDITING FOR RISK

An internal quality auditor for ABC Company has been assigned to audit a welding process for one of the company's products. This particular process welds parts *A* and *B* together to form a subassembly that goes into a final assembly that is shipped to the customer. Parts *A* and *B* can be welded into two different configurations depending on their assembly. This process is governed by Work Instruction 2018, Welding of A/B Subassembly Configuration 1. Personal protective equipment required for the operation is identified in a separate safety-related standard operating procedure.

What the Auditor Witnesses:

The operator is welding part *A* to part *B* per Work Instruction 2018, R2, Welding of A/B Subassembly Configuration 1. The welding operation is underway with sparks flying in the immediate vicinity. The operator is wearing a hood with visor, fire retardant smock, gloves, and steel-toed shoes. The auditor also notices a small puddle of oil on the floor nearby.

During the interview process, the auditor learns that this particular operator started out as a machinist with the company but about three years ago went back to school to learn welding. The operator is found to be knowledgeable of the process and following the work instructions. Training records confirm that the operator has been trained to Work Instruction 2018. It is also noted that while the operator is using the current revision of the related work instruction, drawings and work instruction for the next job in queue are also out on a table in the work area.

(Continued)

(*Continued*)

CASE IN POINT 3.1: AUDITING FOR RISK

At this point in the audit there is no evidence of nonconformance; however the following risks were identified:

- Hazards: sparks and pool of oil
- Risks: slipping, fire
- Other risks: making the wrong subassembly by picking up the wrong work instructions

Additionally, the auditor should confirm the following to determine if there is full conformance or possibly other process related risks:

- Review the safety SOP to determine if the PPE being worn by operator is what is required.
- For technical activities such as welding, training is a two-step process. First learn the skill (welding, auditing, inspection, and so on) then train to apply that skill on a particular job (Work Instruction 2018). Confirm not just operator's training to Work Instruction 2018 but also confirm graduation/accreditation from school as being competent to actually do welding.

This case is an example of an audit that combines elements of both conformance and risk. Once the report has been issued, a risk assessment should be done for each finding of risk to determine what actions need be taken (if any) to address the identified risks.

4

Data and Trend Analysis

Managing risk also means auditors must be trained in recognizing trends in process output data that are reported. Successful auditors of the future will also have a clear understanding of basic statistics, process capability, and data analysis, in addition to comprehensive auditing skills.

STATISTICAL AND DATA ANALYSIS TOOLS

A process can be thought of as an activity that transforms inputs into outputs. Inputs might come from any or all of the 6Ms as shown in Figure 4.1. Both inputs and outputs are monitored, recorded, and analyzed.

Process Capability: Cp vs. Cpk

Process capability is the assessment of the ability of a process to consistently meet or exceed customer requirements. For those desiring an examination of the basic statistics that lead into process capability analysis, you can skip to the Appendix and then come back to this section:

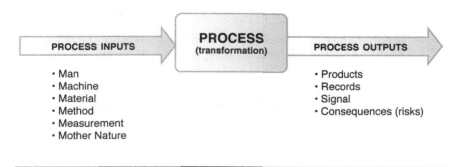

Figure 4.1 Process.

- Cp is the ratio of process width (6 standard deviations) or Voice of the Process (VOP) to the range of the specification limits (Upper Specification Limit (USL) minus Lower Specification Limit (LSL)) which is also known as the Voice of the Customer (VOC).
- In other words Cp = VOC/VOP = (USL − LSL)/6 standard deviations.
- Cp tells us if we have the capability to meet the customer's requirements.

Though an important tool, Cp has one significant weakness; it does not take into account the location of the process. In other words, if the process average (x-bar) is not perfectly centered between the upper and lower specification limits, then the process capability will be lower than indicated by the Cp index. This is the reason that Cpk is the more commonly used capability index. Cpk is determined by using one of the two equations below:

$$(\text{X-bar} - \text{LSL})/(3 \text{ standard deviations})$$

or

$$(\text{USL} - \text{X-bar})/(3 \text{ standard deviations})$$

The first equation is used if the process average is closest to the lower specification limit and the second equation is used when the process average is closest to the upper specification limit.

Generally speaking, the desired Cp or Cpk value is one that is higher than 1.33. A Cp or Cpk value of from 1.00 to 1.33 is indicative of a process that is capable but only with tight control. Although the capability index is a calculation that is distinct from control charts, statistical software such as Minitab will often show the capability index as part of their control charts. So what does all of this mean for auditors? When an auditor sees a process with a Cpk of less than 1.33, then the following questions should be asked:

- Is there a requirement for minimum Cpk?
- If not, then why is the data captured? (Data shouldn't just be captured for the sake of capturing data. There should be some purpose.)
- If there is a minimum Cpk requirement, then what is the required response when the Cpk for a lot doesn't meet the specification?
- What are the process monitoring and controls that are in place?

HOW TO ANALYZE DATA EFFECTIVELY

Validation Reports

Validation summary reports can be unwieldy documents hundreds of pages in length containing highly technical language, many plots and graphs, as well as pages of raw data. An auditor doesn't have to be an engineering genius to review validation reports; just follow a simple strategy. A validation report should have an associated validation protocol or some other document that defines (1) what elements should be in the report, (2) what the criteria are for success, and (3) what the validated set-up is (equipment, settings, work instructions, and so forth). The first step is to ensure that the protocol and report are both signed by all of the parties mandated by organizational procedure. Next confirm that all the elements that should be in the report are included. Confirm that if the validation is deemed successful then all of the critical parameters are recorded as meeting the required parameters per the related protocol. Confirm that any deviations from expected results are responded to according to organizational procedure (deviation form, customer notification, and so forth). Confirm, if possible, that validated state is reflected in the production equipment settings for the process that has been validated. These are by no means the only things that you can check when reviewing a validation report, but rather simple guidelines to allow an auditor without a highly technical background to give a thorough review.

Summarizing

When analyzing data, auditors must be able to:

- Read and understand various types of charts and graphs
- Recognize trends
- Understand process capability

They must also be able to question process owners about controls and response plans in place when a process goes either out of specification or out of control.

AUDITORS AND DATA ANALYSIS

Measurable Goals and Objectives

It is also important for auditors to recognize when (strategic) goals, (tactical) objectives, and metrics don't align properly. A goal can be thought of as a statement of what is to be accomplished. An objective may be thought of as how we will know when we have accomplished the goal or a requirement, and metrics are verification of the actual accomplishment. Let's look at a simple example of a plastic hose pressure tester:

> **Goal**: Pressure test a hose
>
> **Objective**: Ability to achieve a pressure between 200–240psi
>
> **Metric**: Pressure gage reading

As an auditor reviewing records you will want to trace from the completed record back up to the related work instruction, then to the validation report/test document to confirm correct and consistent settings/specifications.

From an overall organizational standpoint, the same rules and definitions apply:

> **Goal**: Go from fourth to second largest industry service provider in three years
>
> **Objective**: Increase percentage of market share
>
> **Metric**: Industry ranking in market share

Leading Indicators

Whenever possible, an organization will want to keep track of leading (process inputs) as well as lagging (process outputs as in the examples above) indicators so that special causes may be identified early and eliminated before defective product is produced.

As an auditor you will want to ascertain from the auditee how enterprise-level goals flow down to lower levels of the organization to become measurable goals and objectives. You will also want to challenge the metrics chosen (both leading and lagging) and how they are used.

CASE IN POINT 4.1: MEASURABLE GOALS AND OBJECTIVES

ABC Company recently received survey results showing that their customer satisfaction ratings had dropped to 73%, much lower than the 90% corporate goal. In order to improve their customer satisfaction rating, ABC management brainstormed as to which attributes of their product delivery were most important to their customers. What they came up with were on-time delivery, quality, cost, and more diverse purchase options. It was decided that on-time delivery, quality, and cost could be acted upon immediately. Expanding on product offerings, while important, was more of a medium- to long-term project. Lean-Six Sigma and other improvement methodologies were implemented to increase efficiencies, improve quality at the source, and reduce cycle time. These improvements, in turn, drove down costs and ABC Company was able to pass those savings on to the customer. In this case, for ABC Company:

Goal: Increase customer satisfaction

Objective: Survey satisfaction rating

Metric(s): On-time delivery (OTD), quality, cost

It should be noted that there will be lower-level metrics such as scrap, production yield, unscheduled maintenance, and others that support and act as leading indicators for the OTD, quality, and cost metrics identified above.

5

Root Cause Analysis and Corrective Action

HOW TO ACCOMPLISH SUCCESSFUL ROOT CAUSE ANALYSIS (RCA)

So what do you do when an audit or other quality monitoring system finds an issue of concern? The answer is root cause analysis. Root cause is the first, most principal cause of an event. Root cause analysis is the process of determining the root cause of a particular event. This event can have occurred in the past (discovered by audit finding) or be expected in the future (data and trend analysis); the event can be either positive or negative. Before root cause analysis can begin, three things must be confirmed:

1. Facts must be verified. Is the situation as previously stated?

2. Incident must be categorized. Is this a nonconformance, a risk of safety or nonconformance, or an opportunity for improvement?

3. Data must be normalized, if possible.

Let's talk a little bit about the third point—normalizing data. If a number has changed (for example, the number of defective parts in a shift), always check the corresponding percentage of defective parts. Perhaps the percentage defective remains the same, but production volume has gone up. Consider the possibility of encountering a typographical or written error non-related to product specifications out of a sample taken as part of an audit documentation sample that includes hundreds of opportunities for error. This is obviously an error but when considering a manual system, should this be considered a quality management system nonconformance? Even a Six Sigma process allows for 3.4 detects per million opportunities. There is no hard and true answer, considering the almost infinite number of possibilities one might encounter during documentation review, but think about it.

THE DIFFERENCE BETWEEN CORRECTIVE AND PREVENTATIVE ACTION

Root cause analysis is often thought to be used only for fixing problems. It can also be used to determine why current state doesn't match the desired future state. As an auditor, one may become involved in improvement projects and should remember this valuable use for root cause analysis.

> *Corrective action* is action that, when taken, eliminates or significantly reduces the impact of the root cause of a problem, thereby preventing or mitigating the effects of recurrence.

> *Preventive action* is action that, when taken, eliminates or significantly reduces the likelihood of a problem occurring or mitigating the effects of occurrence should an adverse event take place. Whenever possible, corrective and preventive actions should be tied to quantifiable metrics so that you have an easy way to see if the action taken has been successful. Quite simply, if the metric moves the desired amount in the right direction, then you have been successful. Leading metrics should also be established wherever possible to give warning if the process starts to go off track again, so that preventive measures can be taken before any nonconformance or risk is created.

RCA TOOLS

Some of the skills needed for root cause analysis are observation, listening, analysis, teamwork, and communication for reporting the results of the investigation. These are all skills that can be cultivated; they are important but not difficult to learn. Root cause analysis can be simple or complex. Training in root cause analysis should be tailored to the level of expertise of the trainee.

The 5-WHYs

The 5-WHYs is a simple but powerful technique. Once an issue is identified, the investigator asks "why" until there is no answer to the question. When that point is reached, the investigator has arrived at the root cause of the issue. Even though the process is called the 5-WHYs, it can be 7-WHYs, 3-WHYs or any number of WHYs that it takes you to determine root cause.

Let's take the example of a person who wakes up in the morning and burns his piece of toast in the toaster.

WHY is the toast burnt?

Because it was overcooked.

WHY was it overcooked?

Because the toaster got too hot.

WHY did the toaster get too hot?

Because the setting was incorrect.

WHY was the setting incorrect?

Um, I don't know?

In this case, there were four WHYs instead of five which brought you to the possible answers below:

- Instructions were confusing
- Slice of bread too thick for settings chosen
- Setting dial not accurate

It is important to note that sometimes the 5-WHYs will direct you to the one root cause and at other times, they may suggest several possibilities for root cause. It is at that point that further analysis would be required, whether that be designed experiments, IS/IS NOT analysis or some other investigative method.

Ishikawa Diagram

Another widely used method for determining root cause is the Ishikawa diagram, developed by Kaoru Ishikawa. The Ishikawa diagram is also called the fishbone (after its shape) or cause-and-effect (after its function) diagram. The Ishikawa diagram starts out with an identified issue as the spine of the fish and then the bones branching off of the spine are the different categories that potential causes might fall into. Figure 5.1 shows an Ishikawa diagram using the 6Ms of manufacturing—man, machine, method, material, measurement, and Mother Nature—as the sorting categories for potential causes.

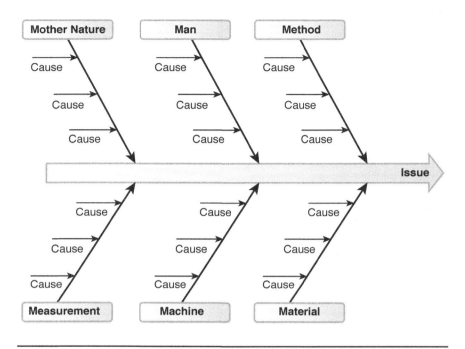

Figure 5.1 Ishikawa diagram.

WHAT ARE THE STEPS OF THE CORRECTIVE ACTION PROCESS

The process for determining root cause is as follows:

- Identify nonconformance / risk / opportunity / gap
- Confirm finding
- Classify the finding
- Normalize data if necessary
- Determine possible reasons it exists
- Determine the magnitude of the (potential) issue
- Identify most likely reason
- Confirm

As data is reviewed during your investigation, relationships between different events begin to emerge. When this happens, it is important to recognize the distinction between correlation and causation. A correlation occurs when change in one factor *A* corresponds with change in another (result) factor *B*. Correlations can be positive (when one factor goes up, the other factor goes up) or negative (when one factor goes up, the other goes down) in nature. There are two possible reasons for a correlation to occur. Factor *A* could be the cause of Factor *B* or there could be a third factor *C* that either affects or is the cause of both *A* and *B*. A favorite simple example of this type of relationship is that during the summer both ice cream sales and shark attacks go up in coastal communities. Eating more than a certain amount of ice cream obviously doesn't cause shark attacks. There is a correlation though; the rising temperature draws more sharks to the area, just as it causes people to want to eat more ice cream. Thus you have correlation without causation between the two events. It is important to determine which scenario you have before trying to determine your corrective action. Otherwise you risk wasting time and resources or, worse yet, putting a fix in place that doesn't permanently address the issue at hand.

HOW AND WHEN TO CLOSE A CORRECTIVE ACTION

A helpful tip when thinking about the process of determining root cause is to think of 5-Ws plus an H[iv]. So what do I mean by that?

What—This is your problem statement. *What* is the problem? *What* is it that we would like to see improved?

Where—*Where* (physical location) is the problem taking place? *Where* would you like the improvement to take place?

When—Time based information. *When* does the issue occur— season, shift, day of the week, and so forth? *When* is the best time to implement the improvement? *When* are you most likely to achieve success?

Weight—How bad or expansive is the problem? How big of an impact can the improvement have on the organization's operations?

How—*How* did the problem escape our controls? *How* can we standardize the improvement, in order to sustain the benefits?

Why—*Why* did the problem occur (root cause)? *Why* does this opportunity exist?

iv Lance B. Coleman, *The Customer Driven Organization: Employing the Kano Model* (Boca Raton: CRC Press, 2015).

Ask the first four Ws and they will drive you towards the H and final W, identifying root cause and preparing you to begin developing corrective or improvement action plans.

Another way to think about root cause is to look at seemingly identical situations such as product lines, manufacturing lines, or customer service representatives (in that they have been trained the same and have the exact same responsibilities) in order to distinguish similarities and differences. Then ask yourself, why is there a problem or opportunity with one and not the other? In other words, what *is* one and what *is not* the other? It is this distinction that will allow investigators to analyze events and draw correct conclusions to identify a true root cause.

It should be noted that sometimes implementing corrective action for a root cause is outside the authority of the process owner. This could be a case where the issue is design-related or a certain way of doing things is contractually mandated. Also, a determination may be made that though the root cause can be eliminated, the cost of implementing the identified corrective action far outweighs the benefits to be gained.

Let's look at a simple example.

CASE IN POINT 5.1: IS/IS NOT

Company XYZ is a widget manufacturer that runs two production shifts—day and evening. A recent increase in widget demand led to XYZ doubling the number of widgets produced during the day shift to approximately 70% of the plant volume. Several months after implementing the new production schedules, it was noted that the production line producing widget *B* had an increase in scrap from the nominal 5% to ranging from 10% on night shift and 15% during the day. At the end of each shift, the equipment was shut down for cleaning and maintenance. All widgets for both shifts are measured during the day shift by the same personnel. Table 5.1 indicates what is the same and what is not the same on the two shifts.

Machine (equipment), (raw) material, method (work instructions), and measurement were all eliminated as potential root causes because there was no difference between shifts. The variance in temperature and time of day differences had always existed so these factors were also eliminated as a potential root cause. Some of the data upon review seemed a little counterintuitive. You would think that the evening shift with less experienced personnel might be prone to having more problems. That possibility was put on hold to investigate last. Volume of widgets produced and production rate were then

(Continued)

(Continued)

CASE IN POINT 5.1: IS/IS NOT

explored as possible causes, which then led back to a discussion of how the increased production rate may have impacted the equipment producing the widgets.

It was eventually determined that there was wear on the part of the equipment that actually formed the widget, causing slight deformation that led to an increased number of widgets needing to be scrapped. The more widgets produced, the more the equipment heated up after hours of use, causing more deformation and more parts needing to be scrapped. After the equipment had cooled down during shift change, the scrap rate again went back down. Because the night shift was not scheduled to produce as many parts as during the day, the equipment never heated up to the point where the scrap rate rose to the 15% level of day shift.

The corrective action was to replace the worn part and reduce the number of cycles to be accumulated before preventive maintenance would be required.

Table 5.1 Same/Not same.

What IS the same?	What IS NOT the same?
• Same equipment	• Different personnel
• Same lots of raw material	• More experienced personnel on day shift
• Same work instructions	• Day shift runs more parts
• Parts measured by same person	• Ten degrees cooler temperature at night
	• Time of day
	• Number of parts produced per hour

CASE IN POINT 5.2: TRAFFIC ACCIDENTS

The main newspaper for a large city in the United States wrote an article on the 10 intersections around the city that had the most traffic accidents. The newspaper used data from the state Department of Transportation (DOT) for its metropolitan area. The data included crashes within 150 feet of intersections as reported by law enforcement officers in 2013. After reading the article, the DOT decided to begin an investigation to determine why these intersections had the most accidents. A team was formed and they met to brainstorm possible root causes and plug them into an Ishikawa diagram, shown in Figure 5.2.

After brainstorming 17 possibilities and populating the Ishikawa (fishbone) diagram, the team eliminated the potential cause of area population because they felt that it was one of several possible reasons for another of the possibilities—volume of traffic through the intersection—and not a standalone possible cause by itself. The next steps were to assemble and review available data around these intersections, then go to the intersections during peak times to take notes. Table 5.2 reflects the observations made based on research and note taking at the various intersections.

(Continued)

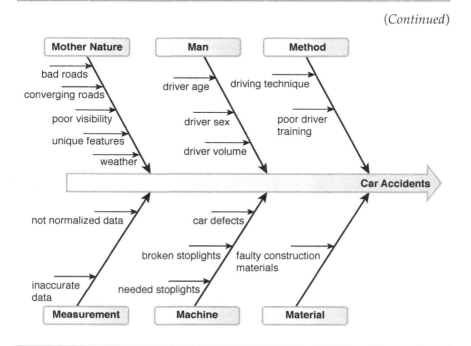

Figure 5.2 Car accident fishbone diagram.

Table 5.2 Traffic accident notes.

Intersecion 1	Intersecion 2	Intersecion 3	Intersecion 4	Intersecion 5	Intersecion 6	Intersecion 7	Intersecion 8	Intersecion 9	Intersecion 10
Student drivers	Heavy traffic	Heavily trafficked	High density neighborhoods	Shopping center	Heavy traffic street	Apartments	Surrounded by apts and single family homes	Lots of companies and employee traffic	Alternate route
Neighborhoods	High traffic entities	Highway exit	Schools	Heavy traffic	Busy shopping center	Narrow street		Near mall	Student drivers
High traffic entities¹	Hwy exit	High traffic entities	High traffic street			Near mall		Major hwy enterance	College nearby
College						High school			
Mall						Student drivers			
60,000 cars	85,000 cars	70,000 cars	60,468 cars	42,000 cars	65,981 cars	61,078 cars	69,445 cars	79,000 cars	61,002 cars
68 crashes	61 crashes	57 crashes	57 crashes	53 crashes	51 crashes	51 crashes	49 crashes	49 crashes	48 crashes
30 injuries	22 injuries	23 injuries	27 injuries	25 injuries	35 injuries	38 injuries	28 injuries	13 injuries	17 injuries

¹ Businesses other than malls and shopping centers such as gas stations, fast food restaurants, and so forth, that have traffic entering their businesses on a regular basis.

(Continued)

CASE IN POINT 5.2: TRAFFIC ACCIDENTS

The first step was to use a scatter diagram of the number of cars through an intersection versus the total number of crashes to see if there were any significant factors beyond volume of traffic through the intersection causing crashes. Expecting to see a fairly straight line indicating a strong relationship between traffic volume and the number of crashes, the investigating team was surprised. As seen in Figure 5.3, the fact that only a slight relationship is apparent between traffic volume and the number of crashes indicates that there are other factors to consider.

The investigative team was able to sort common occurrences between the intersections according to the categories established in the Ishikawa diagram. The data was then sorted and put into the Pareto chart shown in Figure 5.4.

Recognizing that certain factors such as traffic patterns or intersection locations couldn't be changed or were outside of the authority of the investigative team to address, these items were removed from consideration for implementation of corrective action, though included in the final report.

It was noted that egress from high-traffic enterprises around the problem intersections such as malls, movie theaters, restaurants and so forth might potentially be improved. It was further noted that student driver performance was another factor to consider. These were the two factors recommended for implementation of corrective action by the committee.

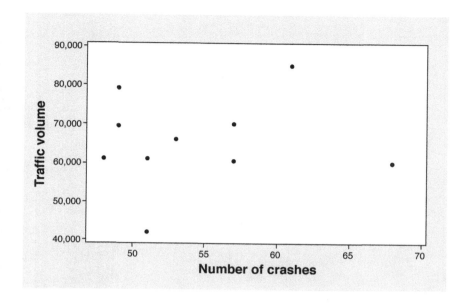

Figure 5.3 Scatter diagram of traffic volume vs. number of crashes.

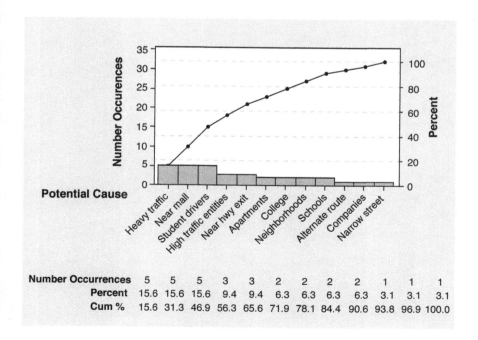

Number Occurrences	5	5	5	3	3	2	2	2	2	1	1	1
Percent	15.6	15.6	15.6	9.4	9.4	6.3	6.3	6.3	6.3	3.1	3.1	3.1
Cum %	15.6	31.3	46.9	56.3	65.6	71.9	78.1	84.4	90.6	93.8	96.9	100.0

Figure 5.4 Pareto chart of potential causes.

6

How Delightful is Your Audit Program?

THE AUDIT FUCTION AS A SERVICE

The Kano model is a theory of product development and customer satisfaction developed in the 1980s by Professor Noriaki Kano, a student of Kaoru Ishikawa (of Ishikawa diagram fame). Kano analysis looks at customer service and the benefits of delivering exceptional value to the customer, whether internal or external, through the vehicle of delightful service. The Kano model recognizes four states: non-performing (failure), basic must-haves (cost of entry into the marketplace), performing (more is better), and exciting or delightful service (surprises and delights the customer). This is shown visually in the Kano diagram shown in Figure 6.1. The x-axis of the Kano model is labeled *desired characteristics* and the y-axis is labeled *customer satisfaction*. Use of this model stresses the fact that the pursuit of delightful service delivery will drive both continuous improvement and business success. Also, the Kano diagram as shown in the Figure 6.5 dashboard can be used as a powerful visual to show progress and remind people of the end goal of delivering delightful performance. The Kano model applies to the audit program because the audit function is a service conducted by the quality department for the larger organization.

WHAT MAKES A GOOD AUDIT PROGRAM

So then what attributes would a delightful audit program have? A delightful audit program is one that does a good job, monitors conformance, manages risk and drives continuous improvement, while continuing itself to improve over time. Such a program will provide delightful results for both internal and external customers. In order to know if you do indeed have a delightful audit program, an assessment must take place. However, doing a quantifiable, accurate, and objective assessment of an internal quality audit program is not necessarily

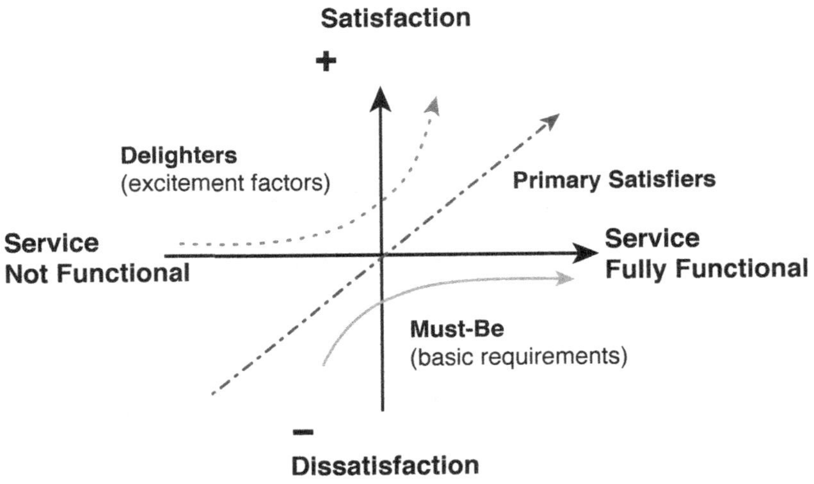

Satisfaction

+

Delighters
(excitement factors)

Primary Satisfiers

**Service
Not Functional**

**Service
Fully Functional**

Must-Be
(basic requirements)

—

Dissatisfaction

Figure 6.1 Kano diagram.

Thanks to Chris Hayes of Impact Performance Solutions for the use of this image.

an easy thing and that is the purpose of this chapter. The Kano model is not the only framework for thinking about the service provided by an internal audit program. Another way to think about a quality management system (QMS) and any of its elements, of which the audit program is one, is the 3-Ds:

- Define the requirements
- Document what you do
- Do what you document

With that thought in mind, I start my assessment of the audit program with audit planning as the largest component. In other words, we are *defining* how we will proceed. I allot 40% out of a potential base score of 100%. Planning is a critical element in any endeavor to ensure that all needed aspects of a given enterprise that need monitoring are indeed reviewed consistently. I also allow points for actually conducting the audits as scheduled. After all, having the best plan in the world is worthless if that plan isn't properly implemented.

Often overlooked in deployment of the internal audit program is that, in addition to monitoring for conformance to requirements, the program should also be regularly assessed for its ability to support corporate and site goals. The audit program should also be seamlessly integrated, as well as an integral part of any risk management program.

Planning—40%

- 5%—All scheduled that should be scheduled (per requirements of the standard, regulation or internal policies)
- 5%—All conducted that were scheduled
- 5%—Percentage on time vs. schedule
- 5%—All non-scheduled (audits not on the annual schedule, that were scheduled to address a concern that was identified) were conducted
- 5%—Annual audit plan approved by site management
- 5%—Audit program tied to QMS evaluation metrics and corporate goals[v]
- 5%—Individual audit plans approved by Lead Auditor or Quality Management, with input from process owners
- 5%—Audit program is well integrated with risk management program

Next I address reporting and record keeping for the *documentation* component. For data to become information, it must be utilized. That is why I also add data analysis as a critical component of this aspect of the audit program. Reporting, records, and data analysis accounts for another 30 percent of a potential base score of 100%. The actual audit results reporting strategy is addressed to ensure that critical and major concerns are immediately reported to the appropriate level of authority. (Safety, legal, and functions issues are some examples of findings that might be reported to a more expansive group of managers that an audit report with no findings or one with only minor findings.)

Reporting, Records and Data Analysis—30%

Reporting—10%

- Reported to site level management
- Reported to quality manager and process owner

---

v Both ISO 9001:2008 and ISO 13485:2003 require that the audit program monitor the effectiveness of the QMS, but rarely is it spelled out how we know that the QMS is effective. Simply stating that a lack of findings means the QMS is effective is not enough. Metrics should be developed to assess the QMS and the audit program should monitor those metrics in addition to conformance to policies and procedures.

Records—10%

- Records maintained—audit reports
- Records maintained—training records
- Records maintained—quarterly/annual summary reports of audit results

Data Analysis—10%

- Summary of reported audit findings and responses regularly analyzed and acted upon

Finally we must *do* or implement what we document. I have focused on having adequate resources, organizational structure, variability, and breadth of impact of the audit program to account for the final 30% of the potential 100% base score.

Some questions to ask in order to evaluate whether or not an audit program has the necessary resources are:

- Do we have enough auditors to do the number of comprehensive audits required within the given time frame?
- Do our auditors have the experience, skills, and education to audit the areas that they are tasked with auditing?
- Do we have the required infrastructure to manage the program: office, computers, supplies, and so on?
- Is there a budget for travel if off-site audits are required?
- Do we have clear authority to conduct audits, as well as the clear support of upper management to do so?

Implementation & Results—30%

- 5%—Do we audit across all operating shifts?
- 5%—Level of auditor training – requirements + actual
- 5%—Amount of audits dedicated to improvement activities[vi]
- 5%—Documented and structured method for evaluating validity and classification of findings
- 5%—Adequacy of resources
- 5%—Use of varying types of audits, that is, process, product, trace, system, element and so on

---

vi If you want to know what improvement auditing is, think of the definition of an audit being an assessment against criteria. Those criteria could be conformance-driven or it could be a desired future state. It could also mean evaluating an area for any of the seven original wastes or even monitoring project results against predetermined milestones.

Once you have arrived at a base score of up to 100%, then we will look at how the audit program provides value beyond verifying conformance and fulfilling a requirement. Basically, the audit program is given credit for opportunities for improvement that are agreed with and implemented. If those opportunities for improvement have a dollar savings value attached to them, then the audit program gets additional points.

HOW TO OBJECTIVELY AND CONSISTENTLY EVALUATE YOUR AUDIT PROGRAM

Next it is time for a reality check. Each major finding against the audit program itself is the worst offense and takes away the most from the base score. Then come major findings from outside sources that had already been identified by the internal audit program, but that have not had successful corrective action implemented. Finally, there are subtractions for major and minor findings related to issues not previously noted by the internal audit program, and repeat findings from the previous year. For the sake of this analysis, the organization can classify the findings presented by outside entities themselves. This can occur when the outside auditor does not classify findings or to provide consistency when plugging external audit results into the model for a rating.

Table 6.1 Value add.

VALUE ADD	
Points	**Description**
+ 5	Observation that leads directly to $1000+ lean savings
+ 2	Observation that leads directly to $1–$1000 lean savings
+ 0.5	OFI that is implemented by area management

Extra credit for value add adds to our total self-assessment score.

Table 6.2 Reality check.

REALITY CHECK	
Points	**Description**
– 5	Each major finding against audit program from outside audit
– 3	Each major finding from outside audit that was previously identified internally
– 2	Each major finding against QMS from outside audit
– 1	Each minor finding against audit program from outside audit
– 1	Each repeat finding from previous year

Subtractions based on results of external audits gives us our final evaluation score.

I allow for points added to the base score as well as points subtracted from the base score per Tables 6.1 and 6.2.

Since typically on a 5-point rating scale which this system uses 3 is considered okay or minimally acceptable (must-be on the Kano diagram), in converting to a 100% scale, 80% or more is the goal and 60% is minimal passing. 90% or more with a minimum rating of 3/5 in every category would be considered delightful. In order to provide consistent scoring/rating, I provide the following definitions to aid with scoring/rating of each category.

GRADING SCALE

5—Very good, better than average, as good as possible

4—Good

3—Minimally acceptable

2—Needs improvement

1—Very poor

0—Nonexistent or almost nonexistent

This model allows for flexibility in that anyone using it may define what each of the above grade definitions means for them. Similarly, the user decides what is adequate or more than adequate training for auditors, as well as the level of resources that are needed to carry out the mandates of their own program. The key is that once it is determined what each definition means for a given organization and tied to a specific rating, the model should be applied consistently to provide reliable results that can be analyzed and used as an input to the continuous improvement program.

One other important consideration would be complete inclusion in the model of the voice of the customer or any specific goals put upon the audit program by its parent organization. In this model, scheduling and conducting audits as required represent the typical mandate put upon the audit program by its parent organization, but may not be limited to that in all instances.

Figure 6.2 shows a graphical depiction of the workings of an audit program following this model. The audit program manager (APM) develops plans based on corporate, site, and audit program goals, which would include different aspects of conformance, improvement, and risk management. In turn, the APM may or may not receive individual audit plans for review/approval dependent upon corporate policy, as well as the experience of the lead auditor. The APM drives the audit execution phase by providing policies, procedures, resources, and credentialing requirements, as well as the assignment of auditors. The APM has audit results reported to them by the lead auditor and, in turn, analyzes and reports results to site management. Responses to the audit are then part of the input to the development of future plans. This whole cycle is repeated, with momentum provided by ongoing revisions to goals and objectives along with analysis of data provided by the audit results. How does your system compare to what is depicted in Figure 6.2?

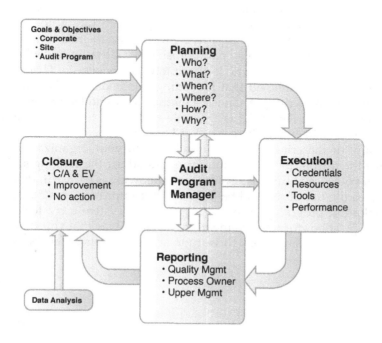

Figure 6.2 Audit program model.

After going through this rating process myself and looking at the score that I gave my own audit program, I found that the initial rating of the program matched my impressions when I first arrived at this site. Also, the improved score, once I had made some improvements to the program during my first year, matched my anecdotal and subjective opinion of where we were at that time. I chose the elements that I did because they are as objective as possible and likely to be consistent from year to year. Use this model as a guide. Adjust the weights for different components of the model according to your own needs. Add, subtract, or change components of the model based on your own experiences.

I do want to acknowledge that there are other important measures of audit program success that I discounted in my model because there are factors other than how robust the audit program is that might be involved in their improvement. For example, the number of customer audit findings going down from one year to the next. Different auditors, stricter clients, improvement in the QMS, and luck of the draw (an audit only takes a sample after all) are all potential reasons for this improvement that have nothing to do with how well the audit program is performing. The same can be said for the reduction in internal audit findings, whether total or major. Also, quantifying monetary savings from audit findings is difficult to do consistently, though Duke Okes made a good argument for that method in his 2011 ASQ Audit Division conference session.

However, these are all key performance indicators that should improve from year to year, as your audit program rating goes up and thus the audit program itself improves. I would use them as an *assessment of my assessment*. I will close by paraphrasing my father-in-law who is not a quality professional, but who is absolutely *quality* people. There is a lot more experience combined that is reading this book than is behind the pen (figuratively) writing it. Give my method a try and let me know what you think. Seen in Figure 6.3 is a sample evaluation form that would be easy to recreate in either Microsoft Word or Excel.

If any of the criteria are not applicable to your organization, then remove them from the evaluation form and adjust the ranking scale. To assist in your use of this assessment tool, following is a Case in Point that illustrates the use of the tool before and after improvements made to an internal audit program. Once you've given my system a try, feel free to make suggestions for improvement or even to tell me that you think I am nuts, if that is the case. I look forward to any comments or feedback.

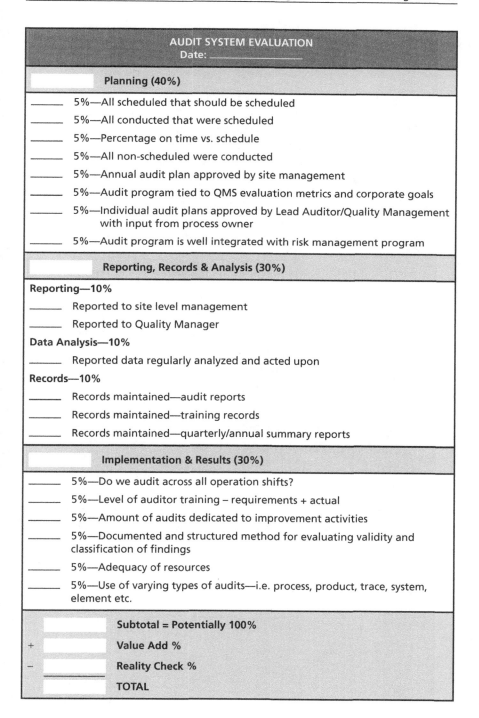

AUDIT SYSTEM EVALUATION Date: _____

Planning (40%)

_____ 5%—All scheduled that should be scheduled

_____ 5%—All conducted that were scheduled

_____ 5%—Percentage on time vs. schedule

_____ 5%—All non-scheduled were conducted

_____ 5%—Annual audit plan approved by site management

_____ 5%—Audit program tied to QMS evaluation metrics and corporate goals

_____ 5%—Individual audit plans approved by Lead Auditor/Quality Management with input from process owner

_____ 5%—Audit program is well integrated with risk management program

Reporting, Records & Analysis (30%)

Reporting—10%

_____ Reported to site level management

_____ Reported to Quality Manager

Data Analysis—10%

_____ Reported data regularly analyzed and acted upon

Records—10%

_____ Records maintained—audit reports

_____ Records maintained—training records

_____ Records maintained—quarterly/annual summary reports

Implementation & Results (30%)

_____ 5%—Do we audit across all operation shifts?

_____ 5%—Level of auditor training – requirements + actual

_____ 5%—Amount of audits dedicated to improvement activities

_____ 5%—Documented and structured method for evaluating validity and classification of findings

_____ 5%—Adequacy of resources

_____ 5%—Use of varying types of audits—i.e. process, product, trace, system, element etc.

Subtotal = Potentially 100%

+ **Value Add %**

− **Reality Check %**

TOTAL

Figure 6.3 Audit program evaluation form.

CASE IN POINT 6.1: AUDIT PROGRAM BASED ON
EXISTING RECORDS

Now let's look at an example of how to assess an audit program based on existing records. Newly certified Company ABC had trouble getting its internal audit program off the ground. A consultant was brought in to improve the internal quality audit program after the company received a finding (one major and one minor) against its internal audit program in each of its two customer audits during the preceding year. All auditors have received formal auditor training; there are no dedicated auditors. Auditing is a secondary (at best) job function for each of them. Upon review of company records, the consultant noted the following:

1. The audit schedule for the previous year was not completed until June.

2. Only 7 of 17 scheduled audits were conducted.

3. Objective evidence that only one out of two opportunities cited were followed up on.

4. Status of scheduled audits was not tracked.

5. Audit forms were completed inconsistently from person to person.

6. Auditor meetings were not held.

7. Audit results not regularly reported.

8. Training record were only available for four of six current auditors.

9. Audit forms were poorly designed and did not flow logically.

10. Audit procedures were unclear and insufficiently detailed.

(Continued)

(Continued)

CASE IN POINT 6.1: AUDIT PROGRAM BASED ON EXISTING RECORDS

Upon interviewing existing auditors, several expressed dissatisfaction with their level of training. All confessed to occasional confusion on how to classify audit findings, how to complete various audit working papers, and when to pursue formal corrective action due to unclear work instructions and poorly designed forms. Some were concerned with having too many audits to do along with their regular workload. Before beginning a root cause and corrective action process, the consultant decided to rate the ABC internal quality audit program in order to provide an objective baseline for comparison against once improvements had been implemented. Figure 6.4a shows how the assessment went. Remember, a score of 60% is minimally acceptable, 80% or better is the goal, and a score of 90% or higher (with a minimum rating of 3 in every category) is delightful.

A rating of 20% definitely placed the audit program in the dissatisfaction rather than the delightful quadrant of the Kano diagram. The next year saw the following changes: Two new auditors were trained, with one working on off shifts and two of the previous auditors received refresher training. Parts of two audits were conducted during off shifts. Current standard operating procedure for audits was totally rewritten, audit forms revised, and auditors trained in order to address previously cited deficiencies. There were no major audit findings against the QMS and no findings of any kind against the audit program itself. Figure 6.4b shows the results of the next year's audit program evaluation.

AUDIT SYSTEM EVALUATION Date: XX/YY/ZZZZ		
14%	**Planning (40%)** *17 out of possible 40 total rating x 40% = (17/40) x 0.4 = 0.14 = 14%*	

__3__ 5%—All scheduled that should be scheduled *yes, but points deducted because schedule not released until June*

__1__ 5%—All conducted that were scheduled *only 7 of 17 scheduled audits conducted*

__0__ 5%—Percentage on time vs. schedule

__5__ 5%—All non-scheduled were conducted *there were no non-scheduled audits so full credit*

__3__ 5%—Annual audit plan approved by site management *developed by QA Manager*

__0__ 5%—Audit program tied to QMS evaluation metrics and corporate goals *not done*

__3__ 5%—Individual audit plans approved by Lead Auditor/Quality Management with input from process owner *no input from process owner*

__2__ 5%—Audit program is well integrated with risk management program *informally tied to risk mgmt program*

| 13% | **Reporting, Records & Analysis (30%)** *13 out of possible 30 total rating x 30%*
= (13/30) x 0.3 = 0.13 = 13% | |

Reporting—10%

__1__ Reported to site level management *only the number of audits conducted reported during mgmt review*

__5__ Reported to Quality Manager *results reported to process owner and QM signs each report for closure*

Data Analysis—10%

__0__ Reported data regularly analyzed and acted upon

Records—10%

__5__ Records maintained—audit reports *hard and electronic copies of audit reports and schedule maintained*

__2__ Records maintained—training records *some training records missing*

__0__ Records maintained—quarterly/annual summary reports *not done*

Figure 6.4a Audit program initial assessment.   (*Continued*)

(Continued)

AUDIT SYSTEM EVALUATION Date: XX/YY/ZZZZ		
10%	**Implementation & Results (30%)** *10 out of possible 30 total rating x 30% = (10/30) x 0.3 = 0.10 = 10%*	
0	5%—Do we audit across all operation shifts? *auditors work and audit only on day shift*	
2	5%—Level of auditor training—requirements + actual *auditors trained but requirements not specified*	
0	5%—Amount of audits dedicated to improvement activities *only compliance based audits conducted*	
3	5%—Documented and structured method for evaluating validity and classification of findings *could be clearer*	
3	5%—Adequacy of resources *adequate resources to implement program*	
2	5%—Use of varying types of audits—i.e. process, product, trace, system, element etc. *only element audits done*	
37%	**Subtotal = Potentially 100%**	
+ 1%	**Value Add %** *added 1 point to score for identified opportunity that was implemented*	
– 18%	**Reality Check %** *–5 for 1 major audit program f, –12 for 6 major QMS f, –1 for 1 minor audit program f*	
20%	**TOTAL** *(f = finding)*	

Figure 6.4a Audit program initial assessment.

AUDIT SYSTEM EVALUATION
Date: AA/BB/CCCC

30%	**Planning (40%)** *30 out of possible 40 total rating x 40% = (30/40) x 0.4 = 0.30 = 30%*

_5_ 5%—All scheduled that should be scheduled

_5_ 5%—All conducted that were scheduled

_4_ 5%—Percentage on time vs. schedule *80% of audits conducted on time; including overflow from previous year*

_5_ 5%—All non-scheduled were conducted *there were no non-scheduled audits so full credit*

_4_ 5%—Annual audit plan approved by site management *attachment in SOP approved by site management*

_1_ 5%—Audit program tied to QMS evaluation metrics and corporate goals *improvement in this area initiated*

_4_ 5%—Individual audit plans approved by Lead Auditor/Quality Management with input from process owner *now input from process owner*

_3_ 5%—Audit program is well integrated with risk management program *findings now classified by risk*

26%	**Reporting, Records & Analysis (30%)** *26 out of possible 30 total rating x 30% = (26/30) x 0.3 = 0.26 = 26%*

Reporting—10%

_4_ Reported to site level management *quarterly and annual summary reports plus input to management review*

_5_ Reported to Quality Manager *results reported to process owner and QM signs each report for closure*

Data Analysis—10%

_2_ Reported data regularly analyzed and acted upon *improvement in this area initiated*

Records—10%

_5_ Records maintained—audit reports *hard and electronic copies of audit reports and schedule maintained*

_5_ Records maintained—training records *all training records current and available*

_5_ Records maintained—quarterly/annual summary reports

Figure 6.4b Audit program post-improvement assessment. (*Continued*)

(Continued)

AUDIT SYSTEM EVALUATION Date: AA/BB/CCCC		
16%	**Implementation & Results (30%)** *16 out of possible 30 total rating x 30% = (16/30) x 0.3 = 0.16 = 16%*	
2	5%—Do we audit across all operation shifts? *parts of two audits conducted on off shift*	
4	5%—Level of auditor training—requirements + actual	
1	5%—Amount of audits dedicated to improvement activities *improvement in this area initiated*	
3.5	5%—Documented and structured method for evaluating validity and classification of findings	
3.5	5%—Adequacy of resources *adequate resources to implement program*	
2	5%—Use of varying types of audits—i.e. process, product, trace, system, element etc. *only element audits done*	
72%	**Subtotal = Potentially 100%**	
+ 6%	**Value Add %** *added 6 points to score for identified opportunity that was implemented*	
− 0%	**Reality Check %**	
78%	**TOTAL**	

Figure 6.4b Audit program post-improvement assessment.

The improvements made to the audit program were substantial and, as expected, are reflected in the greatly improved score. The new rating was three times the original score, well above minimally acceptable (or "must-be" per the Kano model) requirements and within the margin of error (subjective scoring) for attaining the goal of 80%. See Figure 6.5 for a visual depiction of the improvement. There are still improvements that can be made and the low scores in certain areas provide a clear roadmap for improvement. Delightful performance is on the horizon.

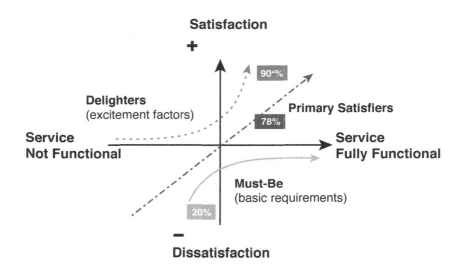

Figure 6.5 Audit program dashboard.

7

Audit Reporting

Generally there are two types of audit reports: one for the individual audit and a second that summarizes the results of multiple audits over time. There may also be reports assessing and detailing contributions of the audit program itself. The audit purpose and scope will determine distribution of the individual audit report. Individual audit reports should include, as a minimum, the following:

- Summary of results to include purpose and scope, audit date(s), audit team members, nonconformances, opportunities, and positive practices

- Finding details, including nonconformances, opportunities for improvement, identified risks, and positive practices

- Request for corrective actions

- Identified risks, mitigations, and residual risks

Audit results summary reports should be periodically reported to site management per organizational procedure. Audit summary results reports, as a minimum, should include:

- Summary of results over time to include any or all of nonconformances, root causes, and opportunities

- Trending and coding of nonconformances

- Identified risks

Audit report distribution should be addressed by organizational procedure, however generally, audit report distribution should be as follows:

- Quality management—every audit report
- Process owner—their individual audit report
- Site management—audit results summary report
- Site management—audit program evaluation report
- Site management—reports relating specifically to safety or other risks
- Upper management—executive summary from the results summary report

Audit reporting is the basis for management decisions. As the main deliverable from the audit process, it is important that the audit report be factual, detailed, fairly presented, and delivered without malice.

8
Charting a Path Forward

NEEDED SKILLS

Auditing is an important skill for auditors, managers, and others who might need to evaluate a situation that they encounter. It is also a rewarding career with many different possible career paths. For an auditor to be successful, though, they must master six skill sets:

- Auditing
- Quality tools
- Continuous improvement tools and methods
- Risk management
- Communications
- Leading and participating in teams

It is also very beneficial for them to bring some technical expertise to the table, whether from experience, education, or a combination of both. Interpersonal skills are another important criteria for the successful auditor.

Auditors have many professional options performing the functions of auditors, lead auditors, trainers, audit program managers, and consultants. Auditors work for manufacturers, service providers, registrars, auditor-certifying companies, and government agencies. I personally got into auditing because I wanted to have a more expansive view of company operations and to meet people working in different departments within my company at that time.

Credentials

To be taken seriously, auditors must have the appropriate credentials. Right now, the two most sought after auditing specific credentials are the ASQ Certified Quality Auditor and QMS auditor/Lead Auditor designations from internationally recognized certifying bodies. The ASQ

Certified Biomedical Auditor has a robust curriculum and is gaining popularity in the medical device and pharmaceutical fields. A non-auditing specific certification that has auditing as a part of its body of knowledge is the ASQ Certified Quality Engineer designation. This is ASQ's most popular certification and is highly respected. You can go to asq.org/certification to learn more about ASQ certifications. ASQ also has a partnership with Exemplar Global that includes QMS Lead Auditor, Principal Auditor, Auditor, and Provisional Auditor designations among its certifications. As of the writing of this book, anyone obtaining an ASQ CQA can pay a nominal fee to take a 45-minute online test to attain the designation of Exemplar Global Provisional QMS Auditor (QMS-PA).

Most auditing certifications are going to require a combination of related education and experience totaling eight years. The term "related" doesn't mean that the education and experience all has to be in auditing; education and experience in fields such as quality assurance, engineering, and so forth are acceptable as well. Whether or not experience is considered related is assessed at the time of application on a case-by-case basis. Having a four-year or higher degree is not absolutely necessary to succeed in an auditing career, but it is becoming increasingly beneficial to have one. This helps establish technical expertise plus gives a broad field of knowledge that can be applied during the audit process. A four-year or higher degree is especially helpful when your goal is to go into either management or consulting.

Table 8.1 is a partial list of job titles and how they relate to different auditing functions. This will vary from company to company but it's a good starting point in determining what type of position you are interested in. The auditor and lead auditor positions have auditing and audit reporting as their primary functions. For the other positions, there will be other responsibilities and the amount of actual auditing done will vary from company to company and position to position. I personally enjoy auditing quite a bit but like to engage in other duties as well, and prefer not to travel more than one week out of each month. I have a job in the medical device industry that allows me to do that. Under the umbrella of my own consulting company, I have had the opportunity to do training in the United States, South Africa, and Europe. Whether you want to work for an employer or as an independent consultant (or both), the opportunities within the profession of auditing are broad and diverse. We each just have to find our own "sweet spot" within the auditing community and then calibrate our credentialing and job search accordingly.

Table 8.1 Job titles related to auditing functions.

Job Titles	Auditing Functions				
	First-party Audits	Second-party Audits	Third-party Audits	Trainer	Program Manager
Auditor	X	X	X		
Lead Auditor	X	X	X	X	
Supplier Quality Engineer		X		X	
Quality Engineer	X	X		X	X
Quality Manager	X	X		X	X
Audit Program Manager	X			X	X
Supplier Quality Manager		X		X	X
Consultant	X	X	X	X	

STEPS FORWARD

The first step in looking at an auditing career is doing a realistic assessment of both your abilities and your credentials. This is an important distinction to make because you may not always be allowed to attempt everything that you are capable of doing. If your credentials don't tell your employer that there is minimal risk in assigning you the job or project, then you won't get the opportunity. So the keys to success are to both deepen and broaden your levels of expertise, and then make sure that your credentials reflect your ability. One way to do the assessment is to create a table having key auditor attributes, plus one column for rating your ability and one column for rating your credentials for each. Table 8.2 shows a table with a listing of 11 desired auditor attributes plus the columns for rating. You will want to rate yourself on a scale of 1 to 5 based on the following definitions:

1—Novice

2—Some experience, confident in the basics

3—Experienced and competent, might provide novices on-the-job (OJT) training

4—Very skilled, might lead audits, and could train others in formal setting

5—Expert, could serve as external consultant or expert trainer

Table 8.2 Auditor self-assessment.

Auditor Attributes	Ranking	
	Expertise	Credentials
Auditing knowledge		
Root cause analysis and corrective action knowledge		
Standards and regulations knowledge		
Quality tools knowledge		
Risk management knowledge		
Industry knowledge		
Lean knowledge		
Technical expertise		
Six Sigma knowledge		
Communications		
Interpersonal skills		N/A

The list found in Table 8.2 is not meant to be all-inclusive but rather a baseline for individuals to modify per their own experiences and research. Similarly, the sequence of attributes may vary depending on the organization and their specific needs. Once the assessment has been done, then the next steps are to identify which attributes need strengthening based on individual goals and determine how to go about doing that.

To conclude, a combination of experience, training, and education is what is needed for the successful auditor to gain expertise. Credentials are what lend credence to that expertise to the outside world. Auditors presently work in manufacturing, service, government, finance, and just about any employment sector one can think of. You have to decide if you want to audit most of the time along with the requisite travel that might come with those responsibilities or if you enjoy auditing as part of a broader menu of responsibilities. This will determine your career path. The future is bright for the profession of auditing as long as we auditors continue to expand on our areas of expertise in order to continue to thrive as a profession for the next 100 years.

APPENDIX

BASIC STATISTICS

A *sample* is a randomly selected group pulled from a homogenous population for the purpose of making observations about that population as a whole. *Sampling* is a means of making predictions about a population under study based on the observations made by taking a sample. Sampling may or may not be statistically valid. Statistically valid sampling as used in business and industry today is often likely to come from a normal or bell-shaped distribution.

Normal distribution: much of the data that we review and analyze relating to our processes has a population that falls into a normal distribution pattern. The nature of this pattern allows for predictive modeling that we use in design of experiments for validation and optimization of processes as well as when determining if a process is capable and/or in control. The two most important aspects of a process output are location (where centered) and dispersion (how spread out).

There are three measurements of a population center:

Mean: also known as the average, the mean is the total of all values divided by the total number of values; mathematically it is referred to as x-bar.

Median: the middle value in the range of values; if there are an even number of values then the center of the middle two values is selected as the median (for example, if the middle two values of a set of numbers are 70 and 71 then the median would be 70.5).

Mode: the most frequently occurring value in a data set.

Note: While there will always be both a mean and a median associated with a set of numbers, there does not have to be a mode.

There are three measures of dispersion of a population (how spread out the population is):

> *Range*: the largest value minus the smallest value in a population.
>
> *Standard deviation*: the *average* distance between each data point in a population. The equation for standard deviation (also called sigma – σ) is σ = SQRT{Σ(x_n– xbar)^2/(n–1)} where "n" is the number of samples chosen.
>
> *Variance*: the square of the standard deviation; this is significant for designed experiments because variance can be added and subtracted.

In a normal distribution, standard deviation allows us to determine where a specific percentage of the population is located, which allows us to make predictions on future behavior:

68.2% of a normal population is within +/– 1 σ of the population mean

95.4% of a normal population is within +/– 2 σ of the population mean

99.7% of a population is within +/– 3 σ of the population mean

As there are no perfect processes, all processes have some amount of variation from cycle to cycle or unit to unit. The types of variation found in a normal distribution are common cause and special cause variation:

> *Common cause:* variation that is normal to the process. Attempts to adjust a process for normal cause variation often makes things worse.
>
> *Special cause:* variation outside or within the three-sigma control limits caused by an external factor. Root cause should be determined and corrective action applied to eliminate special cause variation.

CONTROL CHARTS

Control charts are used to plot data that conforms to a normal (or bell-shaped) distribution pattern. Control charts capture the two most important data for describing a population: the location (where centered) and dispersion. Control charts (Figure A.1) are used to:

- Monitor a process
- Assess process control
- Assess process capability

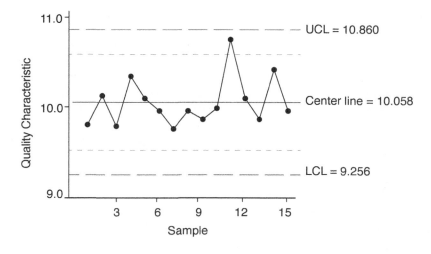

Figure A.1 Sample control chart.

Figure A.2 shows aberrant behavior within the control limits, where a sinusoidal pattern suddenly shifts and greatly increases in variation.

At the start of my career one of my mentors shared this bit of wisdom: once is an incident, twice *may* be coincidence, but three times starts to look like a trend. This advice still rings true whether you are talking

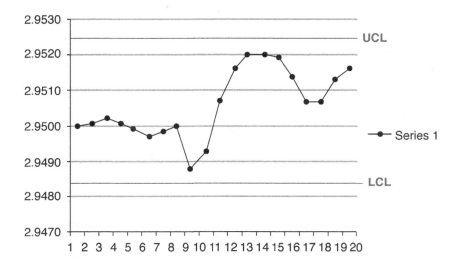

Figure A.2 Control chart showing special cause variation.

about audit evidence that has been collected or data plotted on a control chart. Three data points or even three out of four in one direction over time is something that may bear watching or reporting to the process owner. There are many other variables to consider, but as a rule of thumb this scenario at the very least should precipitate a second look or review of subsequent data points. One of the early pioneers in statistical process control (SPC) using control charts, Westinghouse identified certain data patterns that were indicative of negative trends requiring investigation and these later became known as the Westinghouse Rules. Here is a partial listing:

- Any single data point that falls outside three standard deviations from the process centerline
- Two out of three consecutive points fall between two and three standard deviations from the process centerline
- Four out of five consecutive points fall between one and three standard deviations from the process centerline
- Eight consecutive points fall on the same side of the centerline

Auditors seeing similar trends in data that they are reviewing should inquire as to if the trend was investigated. Also, they should consider under what circumstances would process data cause an investigation to be launched.

Control chart (knowledge) is a huge opportunity for auditor impact that doesn't require a substantial statistical knowledge. In the medical device field, it is a common requirement to report out of specification/ tolerance conditions to the area supervisor. This is so common there is a commonly recognized acronym for it (OOS/OOT). However you would be surprised how infrequently it is required to report out of *control* conditions. There are recognized trends of vacillating or drifting process such as 14 data points alternating up and down, seven consecutive data points above the mean, or six or more data points ascending in value. Similarly, it is even less common to have other unusual trends reported. In addition to reviewing data, the auditor might ask the question, "What do you do when certain trends are noted?" Also, "How do you know what to do? Through training or through a work instruction or both?" By asking these types of questions, potential gaps in the monitoring program may be identified and closed.

While reviewing data during audits I have actually seen a 0.05" measurement indicated as meeting a 0.050" maximum requirement. The obvious issue is how do you know the dimension is in spec without knowing the third digit? At minimum, a measuring device should read the same number of decimal places as the parameter under review and preferably one decimal place more. Besides a possible conformance issue, there is a possible training opportunity or an identified need to improve a piece of equipment with insufficient resolution for the measurement that it is being usedto take.

The *voice of the customer* (VOC) is known to be the needs and expectations of those who purchase or use your products or services, including but not limited to specifications, contracts statement, surveys, and observations. From the perspective of capability analysis, the VOC aspect are the lower and upper specification limits.

Bibliography

Bautista-Smith, Janet. *Auditing Beyond Compliance: Using the Portable Universal Lean Audit Model.* Milwaukee: ASQ Quality Press, 2012.

Curtis, Patchin, Mark Carey and Deloite & Touche LLP. Committee of Sponsoring Organizations of the Treadaway Commission (COSO), 2012.

Manos, Anthony, and Chad Vincent, eds. *The Lean Handbook: A Guide to the Bronze Certification Body of Knowledge.* Milwaukee: ASQ Quality Press, 2012.

Okes, Duke. *Performance Metrics: The Levers for Process Improvement.* Milwaukee: ASQ Quality Press, 2013.

Russell, JP, ed. *The ASQ Auditing Handbook, 4th Edition.* Milwaukee: ASQ Quality Press, 2013.

Tague, Nancy R. *The Quality Toolbox, 2nd Edition.* Milwaukee: ASQ Quality Press, 2005.

Index

Page numbers in *italics* refer to figures and tables.

A

acceptable quality level (AQL), 16
ASQ certifications
  Biomedical Auditor, 79–80
  Quality Auditor, 79
  Quality Engineer, 80
audit checklist development matrix
  (ACDM), 19–23, *20f*
audit, criteria of
  performance standards, 2
  reference standards, 2
audit evidence, categories of, 7
audit functions
  job titles related to, *81t*
  as a service, 61
auditor risk management training matrix,
  34t
auditors
  ASQ certified, 79
  credentials, 79–80, 82
  needed skills, 79
  rating scale, 81
  self-assessment, *82t*
audit program manager (APM), 67
audit programs, xiii
  attributes for good, 61–65
  based on existing records, 70–71
  components of, xiv
  dashboard, *76f*
  evaluation form, *69f*
  evaluation of, 65–76
  grading scale of, 66–76
  initial assessment of, *72–73f*
  internal, 3, 27, 68, 70
  Kano model of, 61
  model for, *67f*
  planning stage, 63
  post improvement assessment, *74–75f*
  rating for, 68
  reality check, *66t*
  reporting, records and data analysis,
    63–65
  value add, *65t*
audit reports
  as basis for management decisions, 78
  distribution, 78
  matter to be included in, 77
  requirements of, 77
  types of, 77

B

Bautista-Smith, Janet, 19
brainstorming, 22, 47, 56
business risk, 27–28

C

career, in auditing, 81–82
checklist, for auditing, 19–23
closure of audit
  confirmation of 4Cs, 9
  pitfalls to avoid during, 10–11
  procedure for, 9–11
  supplier corrective action request
    (SCAR), 11
  value to the supplier, 10
color coding, 29
conducting the audit, procedure for, 7–8
consumer risk, 25
control charts, 84–87
corrective and preventive action (CAPA), 28
customer satisfaction, 61

D

data and trend analysis, xv
  auditors and, 46
  leading indicators for, 46
  measurable goals and objectives for,
    46–47
  methods for, 45
  process capability for, 43–44
  summarizing of, 45
  tools for, 43–44
decision trees, 29
defects, waste of, 14
design of experiments (DOE), 27
Devos, Denis, 38
D. O. o R. S. (documents or documented
    information), 7, *7f*

E

elemental audits
  meaning of, 1–2
excess processing, 16
Exemplar Global, 80
  Provisional QMS Auditor (QMS-PA), 80

F

failure mode and effects analysis (FMEA),
    25, 26, 28–29
  table for, *32t*
fault tree analysis (FTA), 25, 26
5-WHYs technique, for root cause analysis,
    50
flowchart, 19
  receiving process, *21f*
4Cs methodology, 9

G

Great Depression, xiii

H

hard document requirements, 22
hazard analysis of critical control points
    (HACCP), 25, 26, 29
hiring process map, showing enablers and
    risks, *39f*

I

impact, definition of, *31t*
internal audit program, 3, 27, 68, 70
International Organization for
    Standardization (ISO), xiii, 1–2, 10, 22,
    25, 33
inventory, 14
Ishikawa diagram, 51, *52f*, 58
Ishikawa, Kaoru, 51

J

job titles, related to auditing functions, *81t*

K

Kano diagram, 61, *62f*, 71
Kano model, of audit program, 61, 76
Kano, Noriaki, 61

L

lean auditing
  advantage of, 20–21
  checklist, 19–23
  hard document requirements, 22
  integration with audit program, 18–19
  lean receiving audit, 21
  logistics for, 24
  plan-do-check-act (PDCA), 17–18
  principles of, 13–17
  receiving process flowchart, *21f*
  tools for, xiv–xv
  value-add questions, 22–23
Lean-Six Sigma (LSS), 10, 47
likelihood of detection, *30t*
  definition of, *31t*
Lower Specification Limit (LSL), 44

M

mean, 83
median, 83
Minitab, 44
mode, 83
motion, 15
Myhrberg, Erik V., 3

N

non-utilization, of resources, 16
normal distribution pattern, of population, 83

O

on-time delivery (OTD), 11, 24, 47
operational wastes, types of, 13–16
opportunity cost, 14
opportunity for disaster (OFD), 25
overproduction, 15

P

Pareto chart, 58, *59f*
plan-do-check-act (PDCA), 17–18
    PDCA cycle, *18f*
Portable Universal Quality Lean (PUQL) Audit Model, 19
preventive maintenance, 55
process auditing, 4–7
    documentation checks, 6
    goals of, 4
    meaning of, 1
    planning for, 4
    process map, *4f*
    6Ms of, 4–5
process mapping, 19
producer risk, 25
product cycle time, 19
product development, 61
product risk, 27
public safety, events tied to, 27

Q

quality engineer, 29
quality management system (QMS) auditing, xiv–xv, 1, 23, 62
    internal audit program, 3
    process of, 3–4
    QMS risk, 27
    W factor, *3f*
questionnaire, audit, *9t*

R

receiving value stream map, *23f*
registrars, 1
resource allocations, 22

risk
    auditing for, 40
    definition of, 33
    finding classification by, *38t*
risk assessment, 28–33, 36
    form risk matrix, *30t*
risk based quality auditing (RBQA), 25, 35–41
    levels of, 37
    and likelihood of detection, *30t*
    pitfalls to avoid during, 28
    for risk assessment, 28–33
    risk identification and process flow, *35f*
    risk management integration, 33–35
risk-based thinking, 33
Risk is the Compass model, 38
risk management, xiv–xv, 36
    general training on, 34
    for instilling robustness, 27–28
    integration into internal audit process, 33–35, 37
    meaning of, 25–28
risk matrix, 29, *29t*
risk mitigation, 26–27, 34, 35
risk priority number (RPN), 25, 26, 29–30
root cause analysis (RCA)
    corrective and preventative action for, 50, 52–59
    5-WHYs technique for, 50
    Ishikawa diagram for, 51, *52f*
    method to accomplish, 49
    process of determining, 49, 52
    tools for, 50–51

S

sampling, 83
Sayles, Alan, xiv, 36
self-assessment, of auditor's attributes, *82t*
SIPOC (supplier-inputs-process-outputs-customers) diagrams, 19
6 Ms of manufacturing, 4–5, 43, 51
Six Sigma process, 49
stand-alone audits, 37
statistical process control (SPC), 86
strengths-weaknesses-opportunities-threats (SWOT) analysis, 25, 26–27, 29
subject matter expert (SME), 29
supplier auditing, 8
supplier corrective action request (SCAR), 11
systems audit
    meaning of, 1

T

Toyota Production System, 13
traffic accidents, 56
   car accident fishbone diagram, *56f*
   notes on, *57t*
   Pareto chart of potential cause of, 58, *59f*
   traffic volume *vs.* number of crashes, *58f*
transportation, 15

U

Upper Specification Limit (USL), 44

V

validation summary reports, 45
value stream mapping (VSM), 18–19, 23
Voice of the Customer (VOC), 44, 87
Voice of the Process (VOP), 44

W

waiting time, 14
Westinghouse Rules, 86

The Knowledge Center
www.asq.org/knowledge-center

Learn about quality. Apply it. Share it.

ASQ's online Knowledge Center is the place to:

- Stay on top of the latest in quality with Editor's Picks and Hot Topics.

- Search ASQ's collection of articles, books, tools, training, and more.

- Connect with ASQ staff for personalized help hunting down the knowledge you need, the networking opportunities that will keep your career and organization moving forward, and the publishing opportunities that are the best fit for you.

Use the Knowledge Center Search to quickly sort through hundreds of books, articles, and other software-related publications.

www.asq.org/knowledge-center

TRAINING CERTIFICATION CONFERENCES MEMBERSHIP **PUBLICATIONS**

Ask a Librarian

<u>Did you know?</u>

- The ASQ Quality Information Center contains a wealth of knowledge and information available to ASQ members and non-members

- A librarian is available to answer research requests using ASQ's ever-expanding library of relevant, credible quality resources, including journals, conference proceedings, case studies and Quality Press publications

- ASQ members receive free internal information searches and reduced rates for article purchases

- You can also contact the Quality Information Center to request permission to reuse or reprint ASQ copyrighted material, including journal articles and book excerpts

- For more information or to submit a question, visit **http://asq.org/knowledge-center/ask-a-librarian-index**

Visit www.asq.org/qic for more information.

ASQ
The Global Voice of Quality™

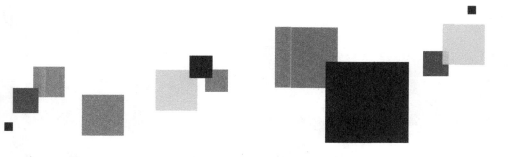

Belong to the Quality Community!

Established in 1946, ASQ is a global community of quality experts in all fields and industries. ASQ is dedicated to the promotion and advancement of quality tools, principles, and practices in the workplace and in the community.

The Society also serves as an advocate for quality. Its members have informed and advised the U.S. Congress, government agencies, state legislatures, and other groups and individuals worldwide on quality-related topics.

Vision

By making quality a global priority, an organizational imperative, and a personal ethic, ASQ becomes the community of choice for everyone who seeks quality technology, concepts, or tools to improve themselves and their world.

ASQ is...

* More than 90,000 individuals and 700 companies in more than 100 countries

* The world's largest organization dedicated to promoting quality

* A community of professionals striving to bring quality to their work and their lives

* The administrator of the Malcolm Baldrige National Quality Award

* A supporter of quality in all sectors including manufacturing, service, healthcare, government, and education

* YOU

Visit www.asq.org for more information.

TRAINING CERTIFICATION CONFERENCES MEMBERSHIP **PUBLICATIONS**

ASQ Membership

Research shows that people who join associations experience increased job satisfaction, earn more, and are generally happier*. ASQ membership can help you achieve this while providing the tools you need to be successful in your industry and to distinguish yourself from your competition. So why wouldn't you want to be a part of ASQ?

Networking

Have the opportunity to meet, communicate, and collaborate with your peers within the quality community through conferences and local ASQ section meetings, ASQ forums or divisions, ASQ Communities of Quality discussion boards, and more.

Professional Development

Access a wide variety of professional development tools such as books, training, and certifications at a discounted price. Also, ASQ certifications and the ASQ Career Center help enhance your quality knowledge and take your career to the next level.

Solutions

Find answers to all your quality problems, big and small, with ASQ's Knowledge Center, mentoring program, various e-newsletters, *Quality Progress* magazine, and industry-specific products.

Access to Information

Learn classic and current quality principles and theories in ASQ's Quality Information Center (QIC), *ASQ Weekly* e-newsletter, and product offerings.

Advocacy Programs

ASQ helps create a better community, government, and world through initiatives that include social responsibility, Washington advocacy, and Community Good Works.

Visit www.asq.org/membership for more information on ASQ membership.

*2008, The William E. Smith Institute for Association Research

The Global Voice of Quality™